SIOP® Training for Teachers

PARTICIPANT WORKBOOK

For use with *Making Content Comprehensible for English Learners:
The SIOP® Model,* 4th edition.

ALWAYS LEARNING

PEARSON

For Professional Development resources and programs,
visit www.pearsonpd.com.

ISBN 97814026-3921-0
NPN 10.11.12

Table of Contents

Azieu, Carlos Maria

Table of Contents

WELCOME/
PROGRAM OVERVIEW

Agreements

- Begin and end on time.
- Mind your technology.
- Actively listen to self and others.
- Participate with mind and heart.
- Ask clarifying questions.
- Help your neighbor.
- Have fun!

Word Wall

You will likely hear the following terms used as you learn about the SIOP Model:

English learners — Linguistically and culturally diverse students who have been identified by language assessments, local placement criteria, and perhaps other measures, as having levels of English language proficiency that may preclude them from accessing, processing, and acquiring unmodified grade level content in English

Sheltered Instruction — A means for making content comprehensible for English learners while concurrently developing English proficiency

SEI — Sheltered/Structured English Immersion; Sheltered/Structured English Instruction

SIOP® — SIOP® Model
SIOP® (Sheltered Instruction Observation Protocol)
The only empirically validated model of sheltered instruction

SDAIE — Specially Designed Academic Instruction in English

L1 — Abbreviation for primary or native language (first language)

L2 — Abbreviation for target language, second language, or new language being learned by student

Common Core State Standards — Adopted by the vast majority of states in the United States, the Common Core State Standards describe student expectations for English-language arts and mathematics in grades K–12 and history/social studies, science, and technical subjects in grades 6–12. (Common Core State Standards, 2012).

List other new terms you learn in the spaces below.

_____   _____
                      _____
_____   _____
                      _____
_____   _____
                      _____

CONTENT AND LANGUAGE OBJECTIVES

Day 1 Content and Language Objectives

Content Objectives

You will be able to:

- Distinguish between conversational language and academic language in second language acquisition.

- Identify the eight components of the SIOP Model of sheltered instruction.

- List characteristics of content and language objectives.

Language Objectives

You will be able to:

- Discuss key points about the factors that affect second language acquisition.

- Share your focus on specific SIOP features based on self-assessment.

- Write at least one content and one language objective.

Day 2 Content and Language Objectives

Content Objectives

You will be able to:

- Identify techniques for connecting students' background experiences and past learning to lesson concepts.

- List elements of academic vocabulary and plan how to include them in a lesson.

- Compare and contrast cognitive, metacognitive, and language learning strategies.

- Determine modifications to teacher speech that can increase student comprehension.

- Identify ways to balance linguistic turn-taking between teacher and students.

Language Objectives

You will be able to:

- Discuss the differences between learning strategies and instructional techniques.

- View and share techniques for teaching content information in ways that students can understand.

- Write ideas for prompting interaction in the classroom.

- Rate and justify your rating on the SIOP protocol for specific SIOP features in classroom lessons.

Day 3 Content and Language Objectives

Content Objectives

You will be able to:

- Attribute ratings to implementation levels of SIOP features in lessons.
- Identify solutions to student engagement challenges.
- Relate research and theories of second language acquisition to the use of hands-on materials and manipulatives.
- Identify techniques for ongoing, formative assessment of student comprehension.

Language Objectives

You will be able to:

- Record the level of implementation of specific SIOP features based on observations of classroom lessons.
- Share ideas orally and in writing to address factors affecting student engagement.
- Describe the benefits of hands-on materials and manipulatives by completing the sentence frame:

  "Hands-on materials and manipulatives are beneficial for English learners because _____."
- Write teaching ideas for reviewing content and key vocabulary.

SECOND LANGUAGE ACQUISITION AND ACADEMIC LANGUAGE

(*MCC4*, Chapter 1)

Levels of Language Proficiency

World-Class Instructional Design & Assessment (WIDA)

Levels of language proficiency represent the arbitrary division of the second language acquisition continuum into stages of language development. The WIDA English proficiency standards label them as follows:

Entering (Level 1):   Lowest level, essentially no English proficiency. Students are often newcomers and need extensive pictorial and nonlinguistic support. They need to learn basic oral language and literacy skills in English.

Beginning (Level 2):   Second lowest level. Students use phrases and short sentences and are introduced to general content vocabulary and lesson tasks.

Developing (Level 3):   Next level of proficiency. Students can use general and specific language related to the content areas; they can speak and write sentences and paragraphs although with some errors, and they can read with instructional supports.

Expanding (Level 4):   Akin to an intermediate level of proficiency. Students use general, academic, and specific language related to content areas. They have improved speaking and writing skills and stronger reading comprehension skills (compared to the Developing level).

Bridging (Level 5):   Akin to advanced intermediate or advanced level of proficiency. Students use general academic and technical language of the content areas. They can read and write with linguistic complexity. Students at this level have often exited the ESL or ELD program but their language and academic performance is still monitored.

Reaching (Level 6):   At or close to grade-level proficiency. Students' oral and written communication skills are comparable to native English speakers at their grade level. Students at this level have exited the ESL or ELD program but their language and academic performance is still monitored.

(WIDA, 2007; as cited in *MCC4*, p. 313)

What factors do you believe affect second language acquisition?

Brainstorm with others at your table. Record your ideas below. Be ready to share with the whole group.

_____

_____

_____

_____

_____

_____

_____

_____

_____

_____

_____

_____

_____

_____

_____

_____

_____

_____

_____

_____

_____

_____

_____

_____

_____

Factors that Affect Second Language Acquisition

1. Motivation and attitude
2. Age
3. Personality
4. Level and type of L1 proficiency
5. Access to the language
6. Quality of instruction
7. Cognitive ability
8. Disabilities

Identify one key idea for each factor affecting second language acquisition.

1. Motivation and attitude

Appeal to interest. Build relationship.
Provide a purpose. Provide ability to succeed.
choices and behaviors are bad → Not the child.

2. Age

3. Personality

Get to know the individual student and be sensitive to their
needs. Differentiating delivery → visual - orally tactile

4. Level and type of L1 proficiency

Expose students to a rich vocabulary environment in both
academic and social. Build vocab exposure with real life
applications so that students will feel confident using their L1.

5. Access to the language

Home. advice families to visit Public Libraries.
Classroom: visuals, read alouds, songs, hands on activities.

6. Quality of instruction

Culturally aware of different cultures we have in the classroom.
Differentiated instruction, having and being able to apply as
a list based on the needs of students.

7. Cognitive ability

Differentiate Instruction — One to One instruction
w/ individual based subjects - know students background.

8. Disabilities

Classroom Connections: Carousel Sharing

Activity Directions:

1. Students work in groups to create posters about the given topic.

2. Display the completed posters around the room.

3. Groups rotate around the room, spending a set amount of time at each poster.

4. Students record their ideas and thoughts about each group's work directly onto each poster.

5. When they arrive back at their own posters, students read how the other groups have responded to their work.

Could you use Carousel Sharing in your classroom? If so, how?

_____

_____

_____

_____

_____

_____

Why would it be beneficial to English learners and/or students who face academic language learning issues?

_____

_____

_____

_____

_____

_____

_____

Conversational and Academic Language T-Chart

Conversational Language	Academic Language

→ O' tol p' tol d mum.

→ Buens, to, Cuns
se ruulm?

Cummins' Model of Language Proficiency

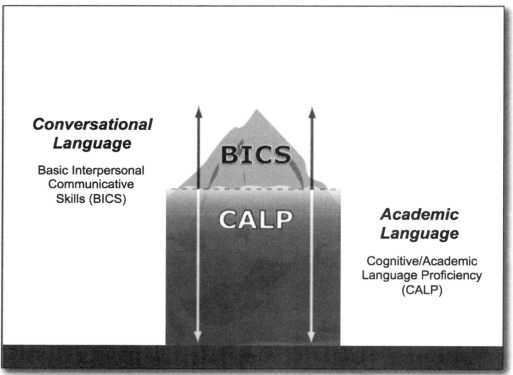

(Cummins, 1994; as cited in Echevarría & Graves, 2011, pp. 9–12)

Compare and Contrast Conversational and Academic Language

Conversational (or Social) Language

Conversational or social language is generally more concrete than abstract, and it is usually supported by contextual clues, such as gestures, facial expressions, and body language.

Academic Language

"Academic language is the set of words, grammar, and organizational strategies used to describe complex ideas, higher-order thinking processes, and abstract concepts"

(Zwiers, 2008; as cited in MCC4, p. 69)

Continuum of Conversational and Academic Language

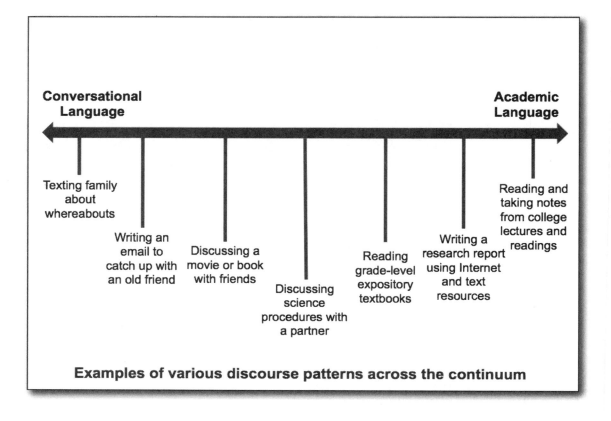

Conversational Language ←————————————————————————————→ Academic Language

- Texting family about whereabouts
- Writing an email to catch up with an old friend
- Discussing a movie or book with friends
- Discussing science procedures with a partner
- Reading grade-level expository textbooks
- Writing a research report using Internet and text resources
- Reading and taking notes from college lectures and readings

Examples of various discourse patterns across the continuum

Profiles of Two English Learners

Read the following profiles of two English learners. Determine where each student is on the continuum for their conversational and academic language in their home language (L1 = Spanish), and their second language (L2 = English) on the next page.

Augustin

- Currently in 5th grade
- Son of migrant workers from Colombia
- Had 1–2 years of formal schooling in Colombia in three different schools
- Has yet to learn to read in English
- While playing at recess, switches back and forth between Spanish and English with his friends
- Is frustrated by school because, "I don't understand what the teacher is saying."

Graciela

- Was born in the United States
- Speaks Spanish at home and English at school
- Is placed in low-track academic classes
- Has difficulty in every class except art, in which she excels
- Reads and writes about 2 years below grade level in English
- Does not read or write in Spanish
- Is in 9th grade and is worried about graduating from high school

Profiles of Two English Learners: Continuum of Conversational and Academic Language

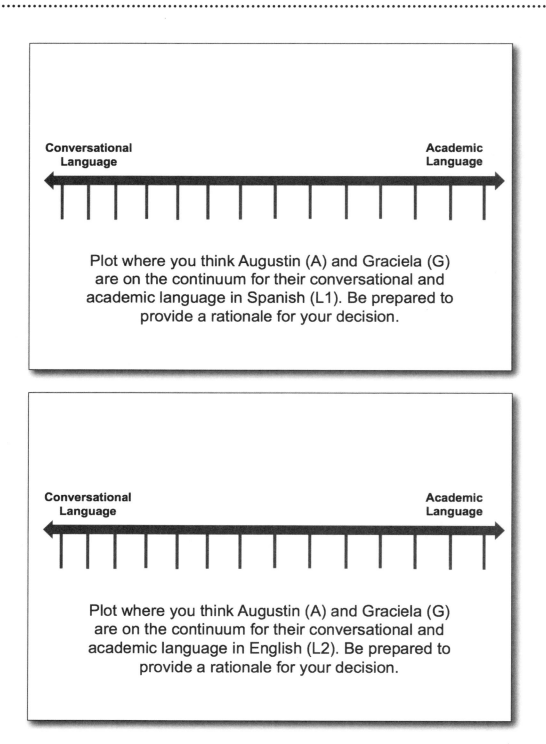

Conversational Language — Academic Language

Plot where you think Augustin (A) and Graciela (G) are on the continuum for their conversational and academic language in Spanish (L1). Be prepared to provide a rationale for your decision.

Conversational Language — Academic Language

Plot where you think Augustin (A) and Graciela (G) are on the continuum for their conversational and academic language in English (L2). Be prepared to provide a rationale for your decision.

Key Concepts in Understanding Cummins' Model of Academic Language

- *clues Included communication*
- **Contextually-Embedded Communication:** Meaning can be derived from a variety of clues, such as gestures, pictures and illustrations, realia, demonstrations, and feedback.
- *Clues not included*
- **Context-Reduced Communication:** Meaning relies primarily on linguistic messages or written texts, which give few if any contextual clues, such as lectures, reading a text, and worksheets.

- **Cognitively Demanding:** A task such as listening to a lecture or reading an expository text on an unfamiliar topic is cognitively demanding.

- **Cognitively Undemanding:** A task that can be performed with little or no conscious thought, such as reciting one's own name and phone number, is cognitively undemanding.

(Cummins, 1981; as cited in Echevarría & Graves, 2011, pp. 32–33)

Cummins' Model of Academic Language

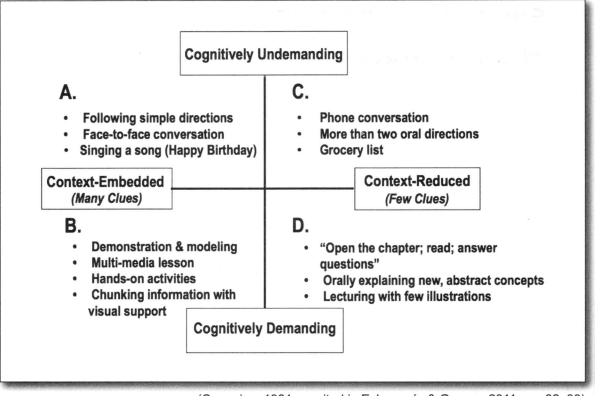

Cognitively Undemanding

A.
- Following simple directions
- Face-to-face conversation
- Singing a song (Happy Birthday)

C.
- Phone conversation
- More than two oral directions
- Grocery list

Context-Embedded
(Many Clues)

Context-Reduced
(Few Clues)

B.
- Demonstration & modeling
- Multi-media lesson
- Hands-on activities
- Chunking information with visual support

D.
- "Open the chapter; read; answer questions"
- Orally explaining new, abstract concepts
- Lecturing with few illustrations

Cognitively Demanding

(Cummins, 1981; as cited in Echevarría & Graves, 2011, pp. 32–33)

Four Quadrant Activity

Label each activity A, B, C, or D to indicate which quadrant it belongs in.

_____ Completing a book's end-of-the-chapter test

_____ Following someone else's Facebook conversations

_____ Following daily classroom procedures or routines

_____ Using manipulatives during a lesson

_____ Greeting your teachers

_____ Following a simple recipe without pictures or illustrations

_____ Reading directions on how to use a new product

_____ Group work with specifically assigned partners/group members

_____ Reading a science article with technical academic vocabulary

_____ Completing an assignment or project using a rubric

_____ Homework at student's instructional level

_____ Role-playing a character's response with a classmate

_____ Learning new content that is unrelated to previous lessons

	Context-Embedded	Context-Reduced
Cognitively Undemanding	**A** • Following daily classroom procedures or routines • Greeting your teachers	**C** • Following a simple recipe with no pictures • Following someone else's Facebook conversations • Reading directions on how to use a new product
Cognitively Demanding	**B** • Using manipulatives during a lesson • Group work with specifically assigned partners/group members • Role-playing a character's response with a classmate • Completing an assignment or project using a rubric	**D** • Homework at student's instructional level • Completing a book's end-of-chapter test • Learning new content that is unrelated to previous lessons • Silently reading a science article with technical academic vocabulary

INTRODUCTION TO THE SIOP MODEL

School Reforms and Policies that Affect English Learners

- **Common Core State Standards:** High standards to ensure that all students are college and career ready; adopted by a majority of states in the United States

- **NCLB:** Standards-based instruction, high-stakes testing, school and district accountability

- **Title III:** Funding, language testing, and placement

- **Title II:** Professional development and highly qualified teachers

- **Response to Intervention (RTI):** An instructional delivery framework that is designed to identify at-risk learners early and provide appropriate services to them

What is sheltered instruction?

Teachers scaffolding instruction to aid student comprehension of content topics and objectives by

- adjusting their speech;

- adjusting instructional tasks;

- providing appropriate background information and experiences;

- highlighting key language features and incorporating instructional techniques that make the content comprehensible to all learners; and

- extending the time students have for getting language support services while receiving the academic content needed to be college and career ready.

"In sheltered content classes, English learners participate in a content course where teachers deliver grade-level objectives through modified instruction that makes the information comprehensible to the students while promoting the students' academic English development." (*MCC4*, p. 15)

"Effective sheltered instruction is not simply a set of additional or replacement instructional techniques that teachers implement in their classrooms. Instead, it draws from and complements methods advocated for both second language and mainstream classrooms." (*MCC4*, p. 15)

Comparing Content-Based ESL and Sheltered Content Instruction

(*MCC4*, p. 14)

Content-based ESL/ELD

Sheltered Content

Video: Introduction to the SIOP Model

What is one point you found interesting in the video?

_____

_____

_____

_____

_____

_____

_____

_____

_____

_____

_____

SIOP Model Self-Assessment

Using the features below, mark the box that most closely represents your current teaching practices: D = Daily   O = Occasionally   N = Never

	D	O	N
Lesson Preparation			
1. **Content objectives** clearly defined, displayed, and reviewed with students		·	
2. **Language objectives** clearly defined, displayed, and reviewed with students		·	
3. **Content concepts** appropriate for age and educational background level of students	✓		
4. **Supplementary materials** used to a high degree, making the lesson clear and meaningful	✓		
5. **Adaptation of content** (e.g., text, assignment) to all levels of student proficiency	✓		
6. **Meaningful activities** that integrate lesson concepts (e.g., interviews, letter writing, simulations, models) with language practice opportunities for reading, writing, listening, and/or speaking	✓		
Building Background			
7. **Concepts explicitly linked** to students' background experiences	·		
8. **Links explicitly made** between past learning and new concepts		·	
9. **Key vocabulary** emphasized (e.g., introduced, written, repeated, and highlighted for students to see)		·	
Comprehensible Input			
10. **Speech** appropriate for students' proficiency levels (e.g., slower rate, enunciation, and simple sentence structure for beginners)	·		
11. **Clear explanation** of academic tasks	·		
12. **A variety of techniques** used to make content concepts clear (e.g., modeling, visuals, hands- on activities, demonstrations, gestures, body language)	·		
Strategies			
13. Ample opportunities provided for students to use **learning strategies**	·		
14. **Scaffolding techniques** consistently used, assisting and supporting student understanding (e.g., think-alouds)	·		
15. A variety of **questions or tasks that promote higher-order thinking skills** (e.g., literal, analytical, and interpretive questions)	·		

Using the features below, mark the box that most closely represents your current teaching practices: D = Daily   O = Occasionally   N = Never

	D	O	N
Interaction			
16. Frequent opportunities for **interaction** and discussion between teacher/student and among students, which encourage elaborated responses about lesson concepts	·		
17. **Grouping configurations** support language and content objectives of the lesson	·		
18. Sufficient **wait time for student responses** consistently provided	·		
19. Ample opportunities for students to **clarify key concepts in L1** as needed with aide, peer, or L1 text		·	
Practice and Application			
20. **Hands-on materials and/or manipulatives** provided for students to practice using new content knowledge	·		
21. Activities provided for students to **apply content and language knowledge** in the classroom	·		
22. Activities integrate all **language skills** (i.e., reading, writing, listening, and speaking)		·	
Lesson Delivery			
23. **Content objectives** clearly supported by lesson delivery	·		
24. **Language objectives** clearly supported by lesson delivery		✓	
25. **Students engaged** approximately 90% to 100% of the period	·		
26. **Pacing** of the lesson appropriate to students' ability levels	·		
Review and Assessment			
27. Comprehensive **review of key vocabulary**		·	
28. Comprehensive **review of key content concepts**		·	
29. Regular **feedback** provided to students on their output (e.g., language, content, work)		·	
30. **Assessment of student comprehension and learning** of all lesson objectives (e.g., spot-checking, group response) throughout the lesson	·	✓	

LESSON PREPARATION
(*MCC4*, Chapter 2)

Lesson Preparation Features

1. **Content objectives** clearly defined, displayed, and reviewed with students } *in student language*
2. **Language objectives** clearly defined, displayed, and reviewed with students
3. **Content concepts** appropriate for age and educational background level of students
4. **Supplementary materials** used to a high degree, making the lesson clear and meaningful
5. **Adaptation of content** to all levels of student proficiency
6. **Meaningful activities** that integrate lesson concepts with language practice opportunities for reading, writing, listening, and/or speaking

③ → What does this remind you of?

⑥ → q' tapa significado para los alumnos → concimos, etc..

. what I heard the teacher said was - - - - -

. Essential questions → cloze sentences ..
    Ej. 3 stages of water.
    → The 3 stages of water are ___ ___ and ..

(MCC4, pp. 26–44)

Why should content and language objectives be . . . ?

Defined and Posted: _____

_____

Observable: _____

_____

Measurable: _____

_____

Displayed: _____

_____

Reviewed: _____

_____

Written in a manner that is accessible for all students: _____

_____

Why are language objectives important for English learners?

- Clearly planned and stated goals incorporate techniques to develop and support students' language development.

- Language objectives focus on developing students' vocabulary, reading comprehension skills, the writing process, or any other core component of language competency.

Questions to Consider When Writing Language Objectives

1. What language will students need to meet the content objectives in this lesson?

2. How can I move my students' English language knowledge forward in this lesson?

Lesson Preparation T-Chart: Objectives

Compare and contrast the objectives listed for each standard.

- **Standard:** Follow precisely a multi-step procedure when carrying out experiments, taking measurements, or performing technical tasks.

    Content Objective: SWBAT follow multi-step directions to accurately perform an experiment.

    Language Objective: SWBAT orally summarize the steps in an experiment by using sequence words such as first, second, third, before, after, then, next, finally.

- **Standard:** Determine the central ideas or information of a primary or secondary source; provide an accurate summary of how key events or ideas develop over the course of the text.

    Content Objective: SWBAT identify several causes of the American Revolution.

    Language Objective: SWBAT write a letter to the editor stating their opinions on the motives of the American colonists or the British.

- **Standard:** Understand that shapes in different categories (e.g., rhombuses, rectangles, and others) may share attributes (e.g., having four sides), and that the shared attributes can define a larger category (e.g., quadrilaterals). Recognize rhombuses, rectangles, and squares as examples of quadrilaterals, and draw examples of quadrilaterals that do not belong to any of these subcategories.

    Content Objective: SWBAT analyze the attributes of quadrilaterals, rectangles, squares and rhombuses.

    Language Objective: SWBAT compare and contrast rectangles/squares and rectangles/rhombuses by listing similarities and differences between shapes in a Venn diagram.

- **Standard:** Compare and contrast the adventures and experiences of characters in stories.

    Content Objective: SWBAT compare what happens to the characters in a story.

    Language Objective: SWBAT develop a story map of the adventures of characters in a story.

Lesson Preparation T-Chart

Content Objective	Language Objective

Connecting Content and Language Objectives

English/Language Arts Standard	Compare and contrast the overall structure (e.g., chronology, comparison, cause/effect, problem/solution) of events, ideas, concepts, or information in two or more texts.
Mathematics Standard	Add and subtract fractions with unlike denominators (including mixed numbers) by replacing given fractions with equivalent fractions in such a way as to produce an equivalent sum or difference of fractions with like denominators. For example, $2/3 + 5/4 = 8/12 + 15/12 = 23/12$. (In general, $a/b + c/d = (ad + bc)/bd$.)
Literacy in Social Studies Standard	Distinguish among fact, opinion, and reasoned judgment in a text.
Literacy in Science Standard	Follow precisely a multi-step procedure when carrying out experiments, taking measurements, or performing technical tasks.

Write a content objective based on the standard you chose.

_____

_____

What language processes will students need in order to accomplish this content objective?

_____

_____

How might you move students' language proficiency forward during this lesson?

_____

_____

Write a language objective for this lesson.

_____

_____

How will you help students meet this language objective?

_____

_____

When you are finished, share your content and language objectives with a partner.

Four Categories for Generating Language Objectives

(*MCC4*, pp. 33–34)

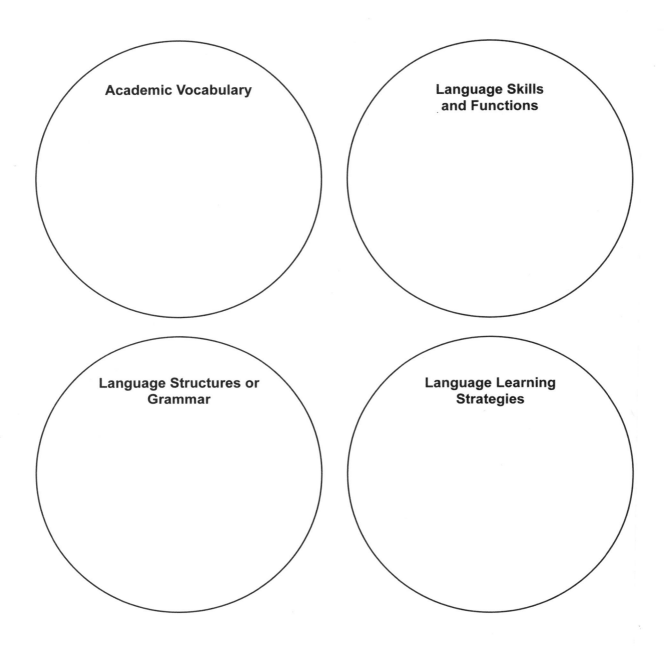

Academic Vocabulary

Language Skills and Functions

Language Structures or Grammar

Language Learning Strategies

Taxonomy for Learning, Teaching, and Assessing

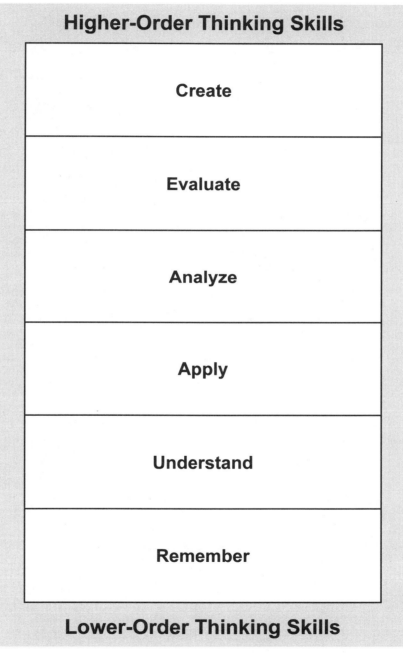

Higher-Order Thinking Skills

Create
Evaluate
Analyze
Apply
Understand
Remember

Lower-Order Thinking Skills

(Anderson & Krathwohl, 2001; as cited in *MCC4*, pp. 124–125)

Process Verbs and Products Matched to the Taxonomy for Learning, Teaching, and Assessing

Level	Process Verbs	Products
Create	compose, propose, formulate, assemble, design, pretend, arrange, create, invent, develop, hypothesize, predict, modify	poetry, story, formula, design, blueprint, play, solution, video, event, newspaper, website, sculpture
Evaluate	judge, evaluate, rate, defend, probe, validate, measure, decide, conclude, determine, justify support, prioritize	investigation, opinion, report, survey, editorial, debate, review, recommendation, critique, verdict
Analyze	distinguish, calculate, question, solve, analyze, compare, contrast, experiment, dissect, discover, classify	diagram, chart, graph, investigation, conclusion, plan, survey, inventory, database, rubric, matrix
Apply	apply, teach, adapt, show, solve, manipulate, schedule, calculate, interview, collect, record, translate	puzzle, drawing, demonstration, diary, report, photograph, quiz, collection, diorama, simulation
Understand	restate, describe, explain, discuss, paraphrase, report, tell, recognize, locate, review, list, locate, calculate	recitation, example, definition, quiz, collection, create a list, explanation, test, dramatization, label, outline
Remember	define, repeat, name, label, record, memorize, recall, match, locate, show, select, group, quote, underline	quiz, labels, definition, tests, worksheets, workbooks, copy sentences

Writing Objectives at Various Levels of the Taxonomy

Use the verbs and products on the previous page to write content and language objectives for SIOP lessons.

Remember!

- Content objectives are intended to develop content knowledge and skills.
- Language objectives are intended to develop academic language.

Let's Write Objectives

Subject: _____   Grade Level: _____

Lesson Concept:

_____

_____

_____

Content Objective:

_____

_____

_____

Language Objective:

_____

_____

_____

Classroom Connections: Inside/Outside Circle

Activity Directions:

1   Students count off in "ones" and "twos."

2. "Ones" create a circle, *facing out.*

3. "Twos" create a circle, *facing the "ones."*

4. Students share their information with the partner they are facing.

5. At the cue, "ones" rotate to the left.

6. Students share with their new partner.

Could you use Inside/Outside Circle in your classroom? If so, how?

_____

_____

_____

_____

_____

_____

_____

How does it support language development for all learners, including English learners and other students who are facing academic language learning challenges?

_____

_____

_____

_____

_____

_____

_____

Content Concepts Appropriate for Age and Educational Background Level of Students

When planning SIOP lessons, use the Common Core State Standards, or your state and/or local standards, and/or learning outcomes.

In SIOP classrooms, although materials may be adapted to meet the needs of English learners and other students who are facing academic and/or language challenges, the content is not diminished.

(MCC4, pp. 38–39)

While content is not diminished, lessons must be planned considering your students'...

- first language literacy (L1);
- English language proficiency;
- schooling backgrounds and academic preparation for grade-level work;
- background knowledge of the topic;
- cultural and age appropriateness of instructional materials; and
- difficulty level of any text or other material to be read.

(MCC4, p. 38)

Supplementary Materials Used to a High Degree, Making the Lesson Clear and Meaningful

Review the list of supplementary materials and resources listed on pages 40–41 in *MCC4*. Then discuss the following questions:

1. Why do you think Feature 4 includes the phrase "to a high degree"? Is occasional use of supplementary materials sufficient? Why or why not?

   _____

   _____

   _____

2. Some teachers think that it will take too much planning and class time to include supplementary materials in a lesson. What would be your response to this concern?

   _____

   _____

   _____

3. Can you think of some ways to minimize the time it takes to gather supplementary materials for a particular lesson?

   _____

   _____

   _____

4. What are some supplementary materials that are not listed here, but you have found them to be especially effective for English learners and other students?

   _____

   _____

   _____

Adaptation of Content to All Levels of Student Proficiency

Skim through four of the teaching and/or differentiating ideas on pages 44–48 in *MCC4*.

For each idea you chose, write a sentence or two about how it provides scaffolding for English learners and other students.

Idea 1: _____

_____

_____

Idea 2: _____

_____

_____

Idea 3: _____

_____

_____

Idea 4: _____

_____

_____

Share your sentences with the others in your table group.

Let's Get Planning: Lesson Preparation

Record your ideas for incorporating the features of Lesson Preparation into your lesson plan.

The content objective(s) for my lesson is/are:

_____

_____

_____

The language objective(s) for my lesson is/are:

_____

_____

_____

How will you ensure that the content concepts are appropriate for your lesson?

_____

_____

_____

What supplementary materials will you use in your lesson?

_____

_____

_____

How will you adapt content to ensure that your English learners can access the materials?

_____

_____

_____

What meaningful activities will you plan to support the content and language objective(s) in your lesson?

_____

_____

_____

When you are ready to write your complete lesson plan, be sure to incorporate the additional ideas you noted at the bottom of page 51.

BUILDING BACKGROUND
(*MCC4*, Chapter 3)

Building Background Features

7. **Concepts explicitly linked** to students' background experiences
8. **Links explicitly made** between past learning and new concepts
9. **Key vocabulary** emphasized

7. = Ejemplo de mutualismo → q' ejemplo puedes presentar la columna dep q' ya explique el concepto.

→ What does this remind you of?

→ Building background is the foundation of learning.
↳ construir algo nuevo en la información que ella ya posee...

Journals: pick 5 a day and five positive and specific feedback...

(MCC4, pp. 65–76)

What is the difference between activating prior knowledge and building background?

(*MCC4*, p. 67)

Activating Prior Knowledge	Building Background

Making Explicit Links to Students' Background Experiences

How might you make explicit links to students' background experiences in your classroom?

Bring back info from smething they already know like il class etc.
Ex: ch →

If students have a mismatch in their background experiences and the lesson topic you're teaching, how can you fill in the gaps and build background?

Ways to Link New Knowledge to Past Learning

- **Questioning Techniques:** Ask explicit questions:

    "Who remembers what we learned about _____?"

    "How does that relate to today's topic/lesson?"

- **Charts/Reference Points:** Outlines, maps, graphic organizers, and word walls/banks that include key information that has been studied or is being studied.

    "Who can tell us about the information on _____?" (referring to a chart, graphic organizer, or other reference point)

- **KWL:** What do you already know? What do you want to know? What have you learned?

- **KWHL:** What do you know? What do you want to know? How do you find out what you want to know? What have you learned?

- **Student Journals:** Have students write a journal entry about their own personal experiences with the topic. Beginning English speakers can draw and label illustrations (using known words) to convey their knowledge and background experiences.

- **Quick-Writes:** Have students quickly write a short response or summary about what they have learned or still have questions about. If students share their quick-writes with partners, they have an opportunity to learn and/or connect with additional information about the topic.

Teaching Academic Vocabulary

Select key vocabulary, terms, or topics from the content and language objective(s) you wrote during the Lesson Preparation session and classify them into the respective boxes below.

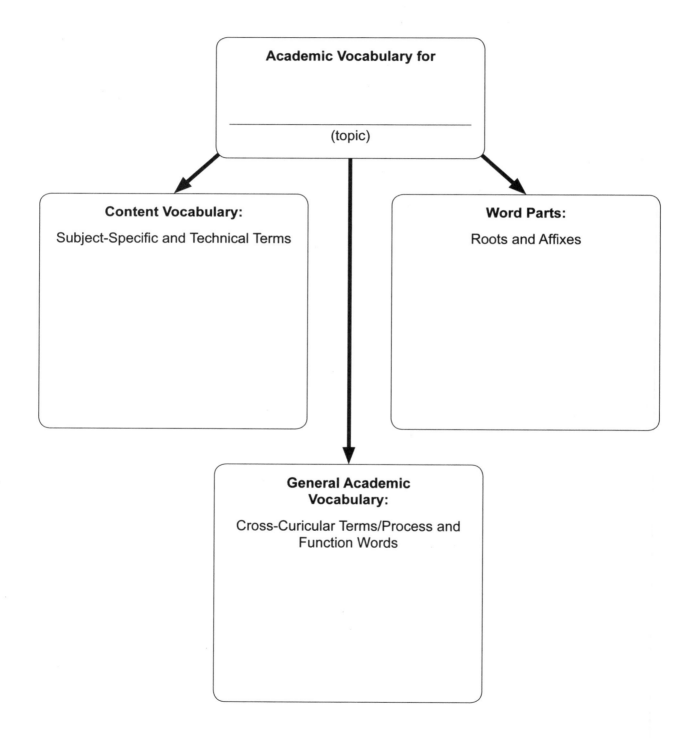

Academic Vocabulary for

_____
(topic)

Content Vocabulary:

Subject-Specific and Technical Terms

Word Parts:

Roots and Affixes

General Academic Vocabulary:

Cross-Curicular Terms/Process and Function Words

Video: What does Building Background look like?

As you observe the classroom video, note evidence of any of the Building Background features being incorporated into this portion of the lesson.

_____

_____

_____

_____

_____

_____

_____

_____

_____

_____

_____

_____

_____

_____

Building Background: What did you observe?

After watching the video, please respond to these questions:

- How were *concepts explicitly linked to students' background experiences* during the lesson?

_____

_____

_____

_____

- How were *links explicitly made between past learning and new concepts* during the lesson?

_____

_____

_____

_____

- How was *key vocabulary emphasized* throughout the lesson?

_____

_____

_____

_____

SIOP Lesson—Building Background

Grade/Class/Subject: 3rd Grade/ Reading
Teacher: Kimberly Howland
Unit/Theme: Theme III, Incredible Stories
Content Objective(s): I can explain the meaning of my vocabulary words by producing a vocabulary flip book.
Language Objective(s): I can listen to and read multiple stepped directions to accurately make

Standards:
Following oral multi-stepped directions.

Key Vocabulary
➤ Awesome
➤ Convinced
➤ Disappeared
➤ Discovered
➤ Impossible
➤ Incredible

Supplementary Materials
➤ Two colors of 8 X 11 paper
➤ Scissors
➤ Vocabulary list
➤ Pencil

SIOP Features

Preparation		Scaffolding		Grouping Options	
___	Adaptation of Content	X	Modeling	X	Whole class
X	Links to Background	___	Guided practice	X	Small groups
X	Links to Past Learning	___	Independent practice	___	Partners
X	Strategies incorporated	___	Comprehensible input	___	Independent

Integration of Processes		Application		Assessment	
X	Reading	X	Hands-on	X	Individual
X	Writing	X	Meaningful	___	Group
X	Speaking	X	Linked to objectives	X	Written
X	Listening	X	Promotes engagement	___	Oral

Lesson Sequence

Objectives
➤ SW (students will) discuss with their partner the content and language objectives, identify the verb in the objective, and share with the class what they will do in their own words.

Anticipatory Set/Building Background
➤ SW discuss with their partner any experiences they have had tending or visiting a garden. "What do you know about gardens?" "Describe a garden you have seen."

Link to Prior Learning

➤ TW (teacher will) remind the students of the theme, Incredible Stories. The title of this read-aloud is Unusual Gardens. Students will share with their partner a prediction about this story. "Howmight these gardens be unusual?"

Vocabulary Exploration

➤ TW and SW echo-read the six vocabulary words and their meanings. TW explain that SW produce a flip book including the six vocabulary words. Each page will contain one word, its meaning, a sample sentence, a sketch and a place to take applicable notes.

Practice & Application

➤ SW create 6 pages following spoken/written directions and modeling for folding and cutting of the pages for the book. SW complete three squares on a Four Corner vocabulary organizer.

Teacher Read-Aloud (and Building Background for subsequent story)

➤ SW participate in a whole group reading of Unusual Gardens. TW ask questions thoroughout to check for understanding and clarification.

Wrap-Up

➤ SW share their flip books with group members. Revisit content and language objectives (thumbs up: objectives were met; thumbs down: objectives were not met).

Building Background Ratings

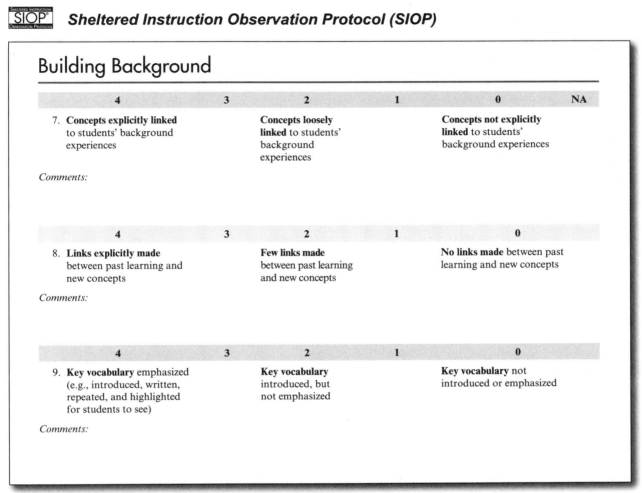

SIOP *Sheltered Instruction Observation Protocol (SIOP)*

Building Background

4	3	2	1	0	NA
7. **Concepts explicitly linked** to students' background experiences		**Concepts loosely linked** to students' background experiences		**Concepts not explicitly linked** to students' background experiences	

Comments:

4	3	2	1	0
8. **Links explicitly made** between past learning and new concepts		**Few links made** between past learning and new concepts		**No links made** between past learning and new concepts

Comments:

4	3	2	1	0
9. **Key vocabulary** emphasized (e.g., introduced, written, repeated, and highlighted for students to see)		**Key vocabulary** introduced, but not emphasized		**Key vocabulary** not introduced or emphasized

Comments:

(*MCC4*, p. 289)

Let's Get Planning: Building Background

Record your ideas for incorporating the features of Building Background into your lesson plan.

How will you explicitly link your lesson to students' background experiences?

_____

_____

_____

_____

_____

How will you explicitly link new concepts with past learning?

_____

_____

_____

_____

_____

How will you develop and emphasize key academic vocabulary?

_____

_____

_____

_____

_____

Building Background: Wrap-Up

- I learned . . .

  _____

  _____

  _____

- I began to wonder . . .

  _____

  _____

  _____

- I practiced . . .

  _____

  _____

  _____

- I felt . . .

  _____

  _____

  _____

- I thought . . .

  _____

  _____

  _____

- I understood . . .

  _____

  _____

  _____

COMPREHENSIBLE INPUT
(*MCC4*, Chapter 4)

Comprehensible Input Features

10. **Speech** appropriate for students' proficiency levels

11. **Clear explanation** of academic tasks

12. **A variety of techniques** used to make content concepts clear

(MCC4, pp. 97–103)

Techniques for Making Input Comprehensible

_____ Use expression and body language.

_____ Speak slowly and clearly.

_____ Use more pauses between phrases.

_____ Use shorter sentences with simpler syntax.

__2___ Paraphrase challenging phrases or sentences.

_____ Give students multiple opportunities to see/hear words.

__3___ Stress high-frequency vocabulary.

_____ Repeat and review vocabulary.

_____ Watch carefully for comprehension and be ready to repeat or restate to clarify meaning whenever necessary.

_____ Be friendly and enthusiastic.

_____ Maintain a warm, supportive affect.

_____ Invite different perspectives of a topic during discussions.

_____ Use gestures and body language

_____ Use visuals — videos, realia, graphic organizers, pictures

__1___ Provide written procedures _with_ graphics!

Comprehensible Input: Analyzing a Lesson Vignette

- Was the instructor's *speech appropriate for students' proficiency levels* throughout the lesson? Please explain.

  _____

  _____

  _____

  _____

  _____

- Was a *clear explanation of academic tasks* provided during the lesson? Please explain.

  _____

  _____

  _____

  _____

- Were *a variety of techniques used to make content concepts clear* throughout the lesson? Please explain.

  _____

  _____

  _____

  _____

  _____

Comprehensible Input Ratings

SIOP® *Sheltered Instruction Observation Protocol (SIOP)*

Comprehensible Input

4	3	2	1	0
10. **Speech** appropriate for students' proficiency levels (e.g., slower rate, enunciation, and simple sentence structure for beginners)		**Speech** sometimes inappropriate for students' proficiency levels		**Speech** inappropriate for students' proficiency levels

Comments:

4	3	2	1	0
11. **Clear explanation** of academic tasks		**Unclear** explanation of academic tasks		**No** explanation of academic tasks

Comments:

4	3	2	1	0
12. **A variety of techniques** used to make content concepts clear (e.g., modeling, visuals, hands-on activities, demonstrations, gestures, body language)		Some techniques used to make content concepts clear		No **techniques** used to make concepts clear

Comments:

(*MCC4*, p. 290)

Let's Get Planning: Comprehensible Input

Record your ideas for incorporating the features of Comprehensible Input into your lesson plan.

How will you ensure that your speech is appropriate for all students' proficiency levels?

_____

_____

_____

_____

_____

How will you make all explanations of academic tasks clear to students?

_____

_____

_____

_____

_____

What different techniques will you use to make content concepts clear to students?

_____

_____

_____

_____

_____

Comprehensible Input: Wrap-Up

What do you believe you already do to make input comprehensible for English learners and other students who face academic language learning challenges?

_____

_____

_____

_____

_____

_____

_____

What have you not tried yet, but might be useful for your students?

_____

_____

_____

_____

_____

_____

_____

_____

_____

STRATEGIES
(*MCC4*, Chapter 5)

Strategies Features

13. Ample opportunities provided for students to use **learning strategies**

14. **Scaffolding techniques** consistently used, assisting and supporting student understanding

15. A variety of **questions or tasks that promote higher-order thinking skills**

(MCC4, pp. 117–126)

© 2012 Pearson, Inc.

Instructional Techniques and Learning Strategies

Instructional Techniques

Activities, techniques, approaches, and methods that teachers use to promote student learning and achievement.

Learning Strategies

Conscious, flexible plans learners use to make sense of what they're reading and learning; these reside in the learners' heads.

In the SIOP Model, we use the term *instructional techniques* instead of *instructional strategies*, so that the term *strategies* refers <u>only</u> to what goes on inside a learner's head during reading and learning.

10-Word Summary Activity

Activity Directions:

1. Find a partner at your table. Decide who will be #1 and who will be #2.

2. Both of you will read the quote to yourselves.

3. #1 will read the quote to #2.

4. Then, #2 will read the quote to #1.

5. #1 will then summarize the quote.

6. #2 will then boil it down to a summary <u>using just 10 words</u>.

"There is considerable evidence from research over the past four decades supporting the assertion that explicitly teaching a variety of self-regulating strategies improves student learning and reading." (*MCC4*, p. 117)

Self-regulated learning *"emphasizes autonomy and control by the individual who monitors, directs, and regulates actions toward goals of information acquisition, expanding expertise, and self-improvement."* (Paris, 2001; as cited in *MCC4*, p. 117)

Strategic Thinking in State Standards

- Use context to confirm or self-correct word recognition and understanding, rereading as necessary.

- Interpret words and phrases as they are used in a text, including determining technical, connotative, and figurative meanings, and analyze how specific word choices shape meaning or tone.

- Determine the central ideas or conclusions of a text; summarize complex concepts, processes, or information presented in a text by paraphrasing them in simpler but still accurate terms.

Learning Strategies

Can tell students *to* *do it...* *not* *Observable* *(in heads)*

Cognitive

Previewing a text

Establishing a purpose for reading

Highlighting

Reading aloud

Taking notes

Mapping information

Self-talk

Finding key vocabulary

Using mnemonics

Metacognitive

Predicting and inferring

Self-questioning

Monitoring and clarifying

Evaluating

Summarizing and synthesizing

Visualizing (making mental images)

Language Learning

Applying reading skills (for example, previewing, skimming, reviewing)

Analyzing and using forms and patterns in English (for example, *prefix + root + suffix*)

Making logical guesses about words

Breaking words into component parts

Substituting known words for unknown

(*MCC4*, pp. 117–118)

Gradual Increase of Student Independence

Scaffolding is . . .

- Teaching that is characterized by careful attention to a student's levels of language and academic proficiency, with early instruction at a level that ensures student success.

- The teacher provides enough support to move students from one level of understanding to a higher level of understanding.

- Assistance is decreased as students are able to access content concepts independently.

- Historically, this has been referred to as the "gradual release of responsibility."

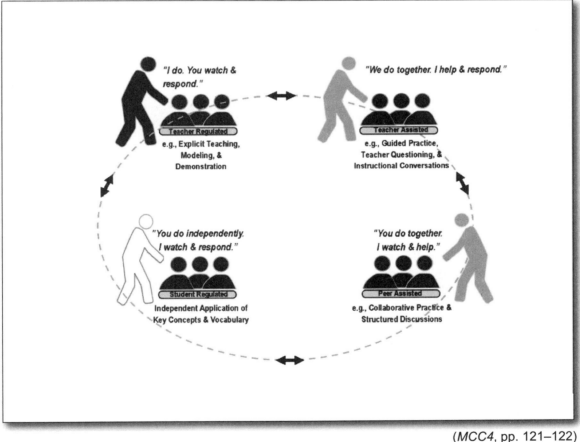

(MCC4, pp. 121–122)

Three Types of Scaffolding

Verbal Scaffolding: The use of prompting, questioning, and elaboration to facilitate students' movement to higher levels of language proficiency, comprehension, and thinking.

- Paraphrasing
- Using "think-alouds"
- Reinforcing contextual definitions
- Providing correct pronunciation by repeating students' responses
- Slowing speech, increasing pauses, and speaking in phrases
- Eliciting more language and information from students

Procedural Scaffolding: Instructional procedures that support or guide the learner and eventually lead to independent work

- Explicit teaching, modeling, and guided and independent practice opportunities with others
- One-on-one teaching, coaching, and modeling
- Small-group instruction with students practicing a newly learned strategy with another more experienced student
- Partnering for reading and content activities with more experienced readers assisting those with less experience

Instructional Scaffolding: Instructional scaffolding provides English learners with access to content and language concepts.

- Graphic organizers used as a prereading tool
- Organizers used illustrate text's organization (such as chronological order)
- Models of completed assignments and sample products (such as posters, booklets, podcasts) to give students a clear picture of the goal

(*MCC4*, pp. 122–123)

Taxonomy for Learning, Teaching, and Assessing

- **Create:** Create a three-day menu of healthy eating.

- **Evaluate:** What is the healthiest food you ate yesterday? How do you know?

- **Analyze:** Compare and contrast the healthy and unhealthy foods you ate yesterday.

- **Apply:** What healthy foods did you eat yesterday?

- **Understand:** What makes a food healthy?

- **Remember:** What is a healthy food?

(Anderson & Krathwohl, 2001; as cited in *MCC4*, pp. 124–125)

Mr. Montoya's Rainforest Lesson

Skim Mr. Montoya's lesson on pages 134–137 in *MCC4*.

Identify the learning strategies that Mr. Montoya is teaching or reinforcing and in which category they fit.

Strategies

Cognitive	Metacognitive	Language Learning

What did Mr. Montoya do to scaffold instruction for his students?

_____

_____

Identify the levels of Mr. Montoya's questions and tasks.

Create

_____

Evaluate

_____

Analyze

_____

Apply

_____

Understand

_____

Remember

_____

Classroom Connections: Gallery Walk

Activity Directions:

1. Students work in groups to create posters about a given topic.

2. Display the completed posters around the room.

3. Tell students that they will be given time to view other groups' posters, and set a purpose, such as reading a poster and adding to it.

4. Students then walk around the room and view the posters in the same way they might view art in a gallery: they choose which posters to view and are not required to view all of them.

5. When time is up, have students return to their own posters and ask volunteers to summarize orally the ideas or comments that were added.

Could you use Gallery Walk in your classroom? If so, how?

_____

_____

_____

_____

_____

_____

_____

How does it support language development for all learners?

_____

_____

_____

_____

_____

_____

Video: What does Strategies look like?

As you observe the classroom video, note evidence of the features of Strategies that are incorporated into this part of the lesson.

_____

_____

_____

_____

_____

_____

_____

_____

_____

_____

_____

_____

_____

_____

Strategies: What did you observe?

After watching the video, please respond to these questions:

How were *ample opportunities provided for students to use learning strategies* in the lesson?

_____

_____

_____

_____

_____

In what ways were *scaffolding techniques consistently used to assist and support student understanding* in the lesson?

_____

_____

_____

_____

_____

How were *a variety of questions or tasks that promote higher-order thinking skills* implemented in the lesson?

_____

_____

_____

_____

_____

SIOP Lesson—Strategies

Grade/Class/Subject: 9–10/Sheltered English 1–2

Teacher: Sarah Russell

Unit/Theme: The Cask of Amontillado/Elements of Literature

Content Objective(s): Students will be able to evaluate the actions and words of the characters in "The Cask of Amontillado" to infer their motivations.

Language Objective(s): Students will be able to use Compare and Contrast Signal Words to showhowthe narrator is unreliable.

Standards:

NVDOEELA2.0: Students use reading process skills and strategies to build comprehension.

2.12.1: Refine pre-reading strategies such as accessing prior knowledge, predicting, previewing, and setting a purpose to ensure comprehension.

2.12.2: Use specific repair strategies such as summarizing, clarifying ambiguities, and consulting other sources.

2.12.3: Plan, monitor, and assess the strategies used to ensure comprehension of a variety of texts.

Key Vocabulary

➤ Unreliable Narrator
➤ Review: Signal Words for Compare/Contrast
➤ Review: Signal Words for Sequence/Order

Supplementary Materials

➤ Elements of Literature © 2005, Third Course/ Grade 9: Holt Adapted Reader (Holt, Rinehart, and Winston, 2005)
➤ Overhead transparency of employment classifieds
➤ Personal white board and markers
➤ Cards to assign groups
➤ Group/student selector spinner (Kagan)
➤ Teach Timer (Ventura Educational Solutions)

SIOP Features

Preparation		Scaffolding		Grouping Options	
_X_	Adaptation of Content	___	Modeling	_X_	Whole class
_X_	Links to Background	_X_	Guided practice	_X_	Small groups
_X_	Links to Past Learning	_X_	Independent practice	_X_	Partners
_X_	Strategies incorporated	_X_	Comprehensible input	_X_	Independent

Integration of Processes		Application		Assessment	
_X_	Reading	___	Hands-on	_X_	Individual
_X_	Writing	_X_	Meaningful	___	Group
_X_	Speaking	_X_	Linked to objectives	_X_	Written
_X_	Listening	_X_	Promotes engagement	___	Oral

Lesson Sequence

Lesson Sequence

Content and Language Objectives

➤ Read content and language objectives to students. Ask for volunteers to read objectives aloud.

Building Background

➤ Break students into random groups of three.
➤ Put transparency of job postings on the overhead. Underline "reliable." Point out that it is an adjective sometimes describing transportation and sometimes describing a worker.

➤ Ask students to write "reliable" in the center of the white board and do a Round Table word web to explore words they associate with "reliable." Use Numbered Heads Together to share out.

➤ Ask students to each write "unreliable" on the boards and try to write a definition and an example of something unreliable (an old car, a friend who can't keep a secret, a dishonest person).

➤ Explain that in this story, we will have trouble understanding what is happening and what happened before the story started because the story teller is an unreliable narrator. What can that mean? Each student writes a guess of a definition on his or her white board.

Guided Practice

➤ Explain that we are going to read "The Cask of Amontillado" now and explore just what an unreliable narrator is.

➤ Break students into random pairs, making sure they are good reading pairs.

➤ Ask what the first step for reading a text using SQP2RS is. Ask what we look for when we survey.

➤ Use Teach Timer to facilitate students spending 45 seconds on each page.

Practice & Application

➤ Direct students to put away their texts and, working with a partner, write three or four questions they think the story will answer.

➤ As students finish their questions, select one question from each group's white board and have a volunteer write it on a transparency. The class should copy the questions on a sheet of paper, leaving space for answers.

➤ Ask the students to classify the questions by the four levels of QAR (Question-Answer-Relationship: Right There, Think and Search, Author and Me, and On My Own.) What levels do we have? What level(s) do we need?

➤ As students finish the question step, direct them to their SQP2RS handout to check what the next step is and write their predictions.

➤ Ask students what is next on the handout.

➤ Call on a volunteer to help the class remember what a read-aloud-think-aloud is.

➤ Students take turns reading the story with their reading partners.

➤ Students work independently to answer questions and correct predictions.

Review & Assessment

➤ Students work independently to use "Sequence/Order" Signal Words to summarize the story.

➤ Students Think-Pair-Share to discuss why the narrator may be unreliable.

➤ Students search for evidence that shows the narrator may be lying to us.

➤ Students Think-Pair-Share why the narrator did all the things he did.

➤ Students work independently using Compare/Contrast Signal Words to write about how the narrator is unreliable and what his motivations were for all of the plot events and for telling the story how he did.

Wrap-Up

➤ Ask for other volunteers to re-read the day's content and language objectives. Ask all students to indicate with their fingers a "3" (met objectives); "2" (made progress toward meeting objectives); or "1" (did not meet objectives).

Strategies Ratings

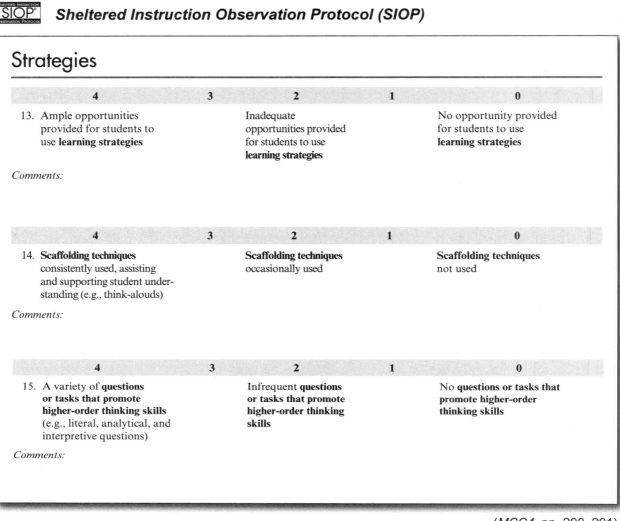

Sheltered Instruction Observation Protocol (SIOP)

Strategies

4	3	2	1	0
13. Ample opportunities provided for students to use **learning strategies**		Inadequate opportunities provided for students to use **learning strategies**		No opportunity provided for students to use **learning strategies**

Comments:

4	3	2	1	0
14. **Scaffolding techniques** consistently used, assisting and supporting student understanding (e.g., think-alouds)		**Scaffolding techniques** occasionally used		**Scaffolding techniques** not used

Comments:

4	3	2	1	0
15. A variety of **questions or tasks that promote higher-order thinking skills** (e.g., literal, analytical, and interpretive questions)		Infrequent **questions or tasks that promote higher-order thinking skills**		No **questions or tasks that promote higher-order thinking skills**

Comments:

(*MCC4*, pp. 290–291)

Let's Get Planning: Strategies

Record your ideas for incorporating the features of Strategies into your lesson plan.

How will you provide ample opportunities for students to use learning strategies?

_____

_____

_____

_____

_____

_____

Which scaffolding techniques will you use to assist and support student understanding?

_____

_____

_____

_____

_____

_____

What questions or tasks will you incorporate that promote higher-order thinking skills?

_____

_____

_____

_____

_____

_____

INTERACTION
(*MCC4*, Chapter 6)

Interaction Features

16. Frequent opportunities for **interaction** and discussion between teacher/student and among students, which encourage elaborated responses about lesson concepts

17. **Grouping configurations** support language and content objectives of the lesson

18. Sufficient **wait time for student responses** consistently provided

19. Ample opportunities for students to **clarify key concepts in L1** as needed with aide, peer, or L1 text

(MCC4, pp. 149–157)

Balancing Linguistic Exchanges

In the Mainstream Lesson:

What do you notice about the balance of linguistic exchanges between students and teacher?

_____

_____

What do you notice about the balance of linguistic exchanges among students?

_____

_____

Who had the most opportunities to speak during this lesson? How do you think this impacts English learners?

In the SIOP Lesson:

What do you notice about the balance of linguistic exchanges between students and teacher?

_____

_____

What do you notice about the balance of linguistic exchanges among students?

_____

_____

Who had the most opportunities to speak during this lesson? How do you think this impacts English learners?

_____

_____

What did the teacher in the SIOP lesson do to balance the linguistic exchanges and create opportunities for students to practice language?

_____

_____

English Learner Grouping Configurations

Review the graphic organizer outlining ideas about grouping configurations.

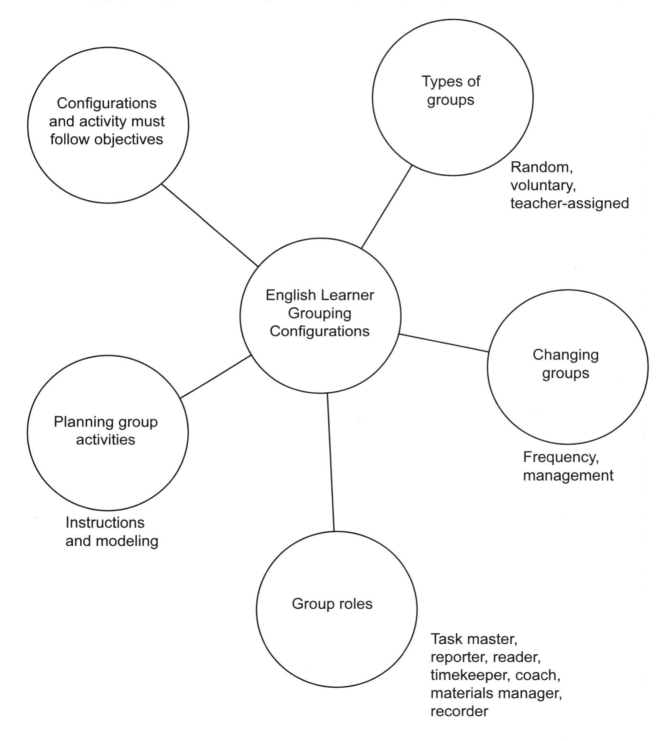

Video: What does Interaction look like?

As you observe the classroom video, note evidence of any of the Interaction features being incorporated into this portion of the lesson.

_____

_____

_____

_____

_____

_____

_____

_____

_____

_____

_____

_____

_____

_____

_____

_____

_____

Interaction: What did you observe?

After watching the video, please respond to these questions:

- How were *frequent opportunities for interaction and discussion between teacher/student and among students* provided during the lesson?

  _____

  _____

  _____

  _____

- How did the *grouping configurations support the language and content objectives of the lesson*?

  _____

  _____

  _____

  _____

- How was *sufficient wait time for student responses consistently provided* throughout the lesson?

  _____

  _____

  _____

  _____

- How were *opportunities provided for students to clarify key concepts in L1 as needed with an aide, peer, or L1 text*?

  _____

  _____

  _____

  _____

  _____

SIOP Lesson—Interaction

Grade/Class/Subject:

Teachers: Rita Villalobos and Suzanne Hanson

Unit/Theme: Place Value

Content Objective(s): SWBAT make, count and write tens

Language Objective(s): SWBAT tell and write the numbers in groups of tens

Standards:
S1 C1 PO8: Construct models to represent place value concepts for the ones and tens places.

Key Vocabulary

➤ Place value
➤ Ones
➤ Tens

Supplementary Materials

➤ Bags of manipulatives
➤ Number cards 0–6
➤ Place value mat
➤ Mix-freeze-match cards

SIOP Features

Preparation	Scaffolding	Grouping Options
_X_ Adaptation of Content	_X_ Modeling	_X_ Whole class
_X_ Links to Background	_X_ Guided practice	_X_ Small groups
_X_ Links to Past Learning	_X_ Independent practice	_X_ Partners
_X_ Strategies incorporated	_X_ Comprehensible input	_X_ Independent

Integration of Processes	Application	Assessment
_X_ Reading	_X_ Hands-on	_X_ Individual
___ Writing	_X_ Meaningful	_X_ Group
_X_ Speaking	___ Linked to objectives	___ Written
_X_ Listening	___ Promotes engagement	___ Oral

Lesson Sequence

Building Background

➤ Personal – How many of you have a jar or can of pennies at home? Do you ever count them? How do you count them?
➤ Academic – Do you remember a very special day we celebrated in January? The 100th day of school! Brainstorm and share with a partner activities of counting that day to 100. TW (the teacher will) show them the 100th Day Mat used that day for counting groups of tens.
➤ Calendar – What do we do every day when we count the days of school during calendar time? Discuss with the students the process of making groups of ten with straws and moving them into the tens pocket.
➤ Introduce vocabulary and objectives for the day.

Lesson Sequence

➤ Dump the pennies out and count them one-by-one with Mrs. Hanson. Help the students brainstorm an easier way to do so, keeping in mind the objectives of the day. Demonstrate how counting in groups of ten can make this easier, especially when the groups are placed in a cup. Allow the students time to take their bags of manipulatives and count them into groups of ten.

➤ Introduce the Place Value Mat and model which columns the groups of tens should be placed in. Also model how to count each column and assign a number to the column appropriately, and then read the number correctly.

➤ Using their cups, the students will work with the teacher to model and count groups of ten at their desks.The number cards will be placed by the students at the bottom of the place value mat to correctly represent their modeled groups of tens.

Practice & Application

➤ With a partner, the students will be given three bags of different manipulatives to count, place on their mats and write the correct numbers on a teacher-made worksheet.

Review & Assessment

➤ Mix-Freeze-Match – SW (students will) match the correct number values (on one card) to the pictorial representations (on someone else's card). Each group will be given time to practice how many groups of ten they have, and what their number is. Each group will share their answers with the class.

Wrap-Up

➤ All groups will share their answers with the class.
➤ Review content and language objectives with students.

Interaction Ratings

SIOP® *Sheltered Instruction Observation Protocol (SIOP)*

Interaction

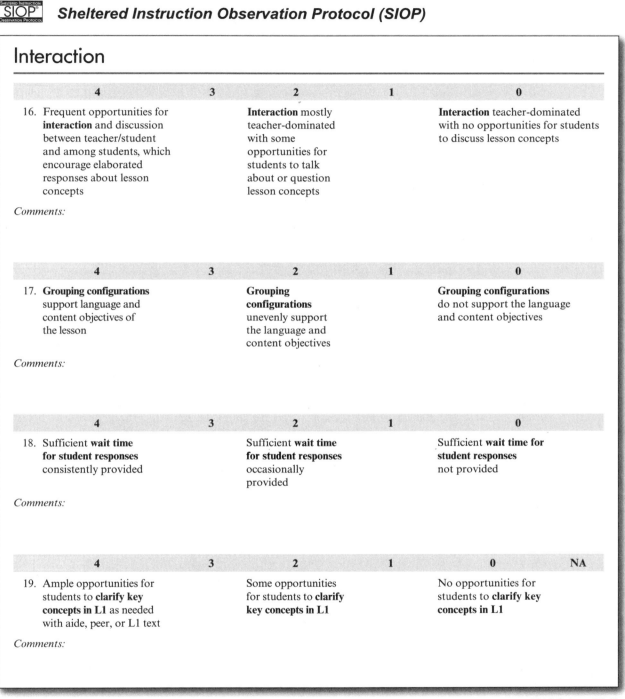

4	3	2	1	0
16. Frequent opportunities for **interaction** and discussion between teacher/student and among students, which encourage elaborated responses about lesson concepts		**Interaction** mostly teacher-dominated with some opportunities for students to talk about or question lesson concepts		**Interaction** teacher-dominated with no opportunities for students to discuss lesson concepts

Comments:

4	3	2	1	0
17. **Grouping configurations** support language and content objectives of the lesson		**Grouping configurations** unevenly support the language and content objectives		**Grouping configurations** do not support the language and content objectives

Comments:

4	3	2	1	0
18. Sufficient **wait time for student responses** consistently provided		Sufficient **wait time for student responses** occasionally provided		Sufficient **wait time for student responses** not provided

Comments:

4	3	2	1	0	NA
19. Ample opportunities for students to **clarify key concepts in L1** as needed with aide, peer, or L1 text		Some opportunities for students to **clarify key concepts in L1**		No opportunities for students to **clarify key concepts in L1**	

Comments:

(*MCC4*, p. 291)

Interaction: Musical Share

Write your favorite ideas for promoting interaction or providing wait time in the classroom.

Promoting interaction:

_____

_____

_____

_____

_____

_____

_____

Providing wait time:

_____

_____

_____

_____

_____

_____

_____

Classroom Connections: Musical Share

Activity Directions:

1. When the music starts, students move around the room.

2. When the music stops, students stop and find a partner close to them with whom to share their responses.

3. Continue the process until students have shared with at least two other students.

Could you use Musical Share in your classroom? If so, how?

_____

_____

_____

_____

_____

_____

_____

How does it support language development for all learners?

_____

_____

_____

_____

_____

_____

_____

Let's Get Planning: Interaction

Record your ideas for incorporating the features of Interaction into your lesson plan.

How will you provide frequent opportunities for interaction and discussion between you and the students and among students?

_____

_____

_____

_____

_____

What grouping configurations will you use to support the lesson's content and language objectives?

_____

_____

_____

_____

How will you ensure that you provide sufficient wait time for student responses?

_____

_____

_____

_____

How will you provide opportunities for students to clarify key concepts in their L1 as needed?

_____

_____

_____

_____

Interaction: Wrap-Up

Describe a class that integrates reading, writing, listening, and speaking.

Looks Like	Sounds Like	Feels Like	Examples

PRACTICE & APPLICATION
(*MCC4*, Chapter 7)

Practice & Application Features

20. **Hands-on materials and/or manipulatives** provided for students to practice using new content knowledge

21. Activities provided for students to **apply content and language knowledge** in the classroom

22. Activities integrate all **language skills** (i.e., reading, writing, listening, and speaking)

(MCC4, pp. 174–178)

© 2012 Pearson, Inc.

Video: What does Practice & Application look like?

As you observe the classroom video, note evidence of the features of Practice & Application that are incorporated into this part of the lesson.

_____

_____

_____

_____

_____

_____

_____

_____

_____

_____

_____

_____

_____

_____

_____

_____

_____

_____

_____

_____

Practice & Application: What did you observe?

After watching the video, please respond to these questions:

How were *hands-on materials and/or manipulatives provided for students to practice using new content knowledge* in the lesson?

_____

_____

_____

_____

_____

How were *activities provided for students to apply content and language knowledge in the classroom?*

_____

_____

_____

_____

_____

How did the lesson *activities integrate all language skills (i.e., reading, writing, listening, and speaking)?*

_____

_____

_____

_____

_____

SIOP Lesson—Practice & Application

Grade/Class/Subject: 8th Grade Physical Science

Teacher: Hope Phillips

Unit/Theme: Newton's First Lawof Motion

Content Objective(s): Students will be able to demonstrate application of scientific observations by recording observations about raisins in the beaker.

Language Objective(s): Students will use the words gravity, buoyant force, rest, motion, and force to explain what happened in the beaker.

Students will make observations about the experiment using the vocabulary words in the sentence frame: "One observation I made is _____."

Standards:

SC8 S1 C2 PO1: Demonstrate safe behavior and appropriate procedures in all science inquiry.

SC8 S1 C2 PO5: Keep a record of observations, notes, sketches, questions and ideas using tools such as written and/or computer logs.

SC8 S5 C2 PO2: Identify the conditions under which an object will continue in its state of motion (Newton's 1st Lawof Motion).

Key Vocabulary

- ➤ Gravity
- ➤ Beaker
- ➤ Buoyant force
- ➤ Observation

Supplementary Materials

- ➤ Beakers
- ➤ Baking soda
- ➤ Vinegar
- ➤ Raisins
- ➤ Teacher-created graphic organizers
- ➤ Self-stick notes

SIOP Features

Preparation

- _X_ Adaptation of Content
- _X_ Links to Background
- _X_ Links to Past Learning
- _X_ Strategies incorporated

Scaffolding

- _X_ Modeling
- _X_ Guided practice
- _X_ Independent practice
- _X_ Comprehensible input

Grouping Options

- _X_ Whole class
- _X_ Small groups
- _X_ Partners
- _X_ Independent

Integration of Processes

- _X_ Reading
- _X_ Writing
- _X_ Speaking
- _X_ Listening

Application

- _X_ Hands-on
- _X_ Meaningful
- _X_ Linked to objectives
- _X_ Promotes engagement

Assessment

- _X_ Individual
- _X_ Group
- _X_ Written
- _X_ Oral

Lesson Sequence

LessonSequence

Link to Past Learning

- ➤ TW (teacher will) show a short video clip of students from yesterday's class doing two activities. Both activities were to demonstrate Newton's First Law of Motion. TW show the two video clips and will then ask the students to write about what they noticed in the video clips. SW (students will) share their responses with each other in "Milling to Music."

Introduction

- ➤ TW explain the objectives for the day. TW tell students that today they will be doing a mini-experiment. During this experiment they are going to make observations and inferences. At the end of the experiment, they will explain what forces they observed. They will also use Newton's First Law of Motion to explain what they observed. TW go over vocabulary for the day.

Modeling

➤ TW give the students directions for the raisin activity. The teacher will add water, raisins and baking soda to a beaker in the front of the room. The teacher will write two observations using sequence words.

Guided Practice

➤ TW ask the students to write one observation of what has happened so far. TW then have the students think-pair-share their answers. When the teacher has decided the students understand what to do, she will tell the students to add the vinegar to the solution.

Independent Practice & Application

➤ After the vinegar has been added, the students will make 6–8 more observations of what they see happening in the beaker. TW walk fromtable to table to monitor the students. When the students are done, TW model for students howto use the sentence starters for their self-stick notes. Then SW write on their self-stick notes and place their self-stick notes on the raisin observation paper.

Modeling

➤ TW review with students what an inference is. TW take an example observation from the poster and make an inference from that observation. TW write the example on the overhead.

Guided Practice

➤ TW pick another observation fromthe chart and write it on the overhead. SW then make an inference fromthat observation and write it on their graphic organizer.

Independent Practice & Application

➤ After assessing students' understandings of the task, TW give them time to choose three more observations. SW: 1) choose three observations and write an inference for each observation; 2) write a sentence using cause and effect to describe their inference; 3) write on a self-stick note and place it on the chart on the board.

Wrap-Up

➤ TW will review content and language objectives with the students and ask for examples of each objective that was accomplished.

Remediation

➤ Students are grouped with other students of varied language and academic levels. TW make frequent stops at each table to see which students are struggling with the content. TW use graphics and graphic organizers to help students.

Enrichment

➤ If students finish quickly, TW ask them to try to explain their observations using Newton's Third Law of Motion.

Final Review & Assessment

➤ Content and Language Objectives: TW evaluate the graphic organizers, the students' written observations, and the written inferences. The teacher will also evaluate the objectives by walking from group to group and asking questions.

Practice & Application Ratings

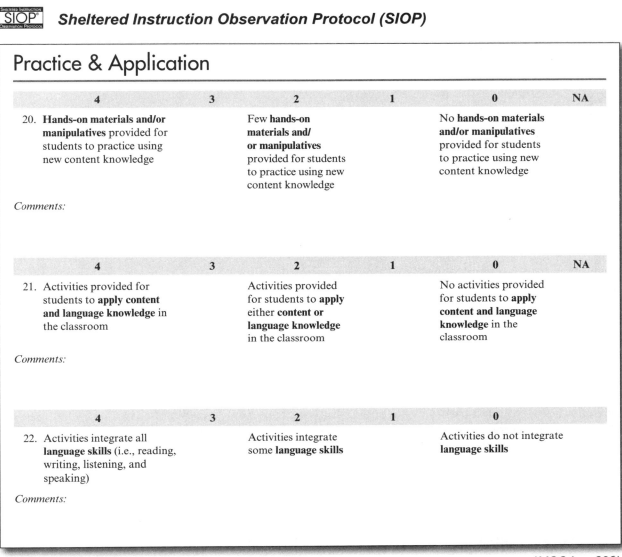

Practice & Application

4	3	2	1	0	NA
20. **Hands-on materials and/or manipulatives** provided for students to practice using new content knowledge		Few **hands-on materials and/or manipulatives** provided for students to practice using new content knowledge		No **hands-on materials and/or manipulatives** provided for students to practice using new content knowledge	

Comments:

4	3	2	1	0	NA
21. Activities provided for students to **apply content and language knowledge** in the classroom		Activities provided for students to **apply** either **content or language knowledge** in the classroom		No activities provided for students to **apply content and language knowledge** in the classroom	

Comments:

4	3	2	1	0
22. Activities integrate all **language skills** (i.e., reading, writing, listening, and speaking)		Activities integrate some **language skills**		Activities do not integrate **language skills**

Comments:

(*MCC4*, p. 292)

Let's Practice and Apply: Jigsaw Activity

Group 1

Standard: Compare and contrast two or more characters, settings, or events in a story or drama, drawing on specific details in the text (e.g., how characters interact).

What	How
Characterization (qualities, motives, actions, thoughts, dialogue, development, interactions)	Character Matrix: In groups, students create a grid that lists the characters vertically along the left side and character traits horizontally across the top.
Content Objective:	**Language Objective:**
Way to demonstrate/present the "How"	

Group 2

Standard: Determine a theme of a story, drama, or poem from details in the text, including how characters in a story or drama respond to challenges or how the speaker in a poem reflects upon a topic; summarize the text.

What	How
Write a summary based on the information gathered that includes: 　a. a topic sentence 　b. supporting details 　c. relevant information	Soul Train/Line-Up: The class lines up according to specific criteria (age, birthday, first letter of name...). "Fold" the end of the line with the head of the line and pair up until each person has a partner. Rotate on cue.
Content Objective:	**Language Objective:**
Way to demonstrate/present the "How"	

Group 3

Standard: Solve real world and mathematical problems involving perimeters of polygons, including finding the perimeter given the side lengths, finding an unknown side length, and exhibiting rectangles with the same perimeter and different areas or with the same area and different perimeters.

What	How
Compare area and perimeter	Graphic Organizer
Content Objective:	**Language Objective:**
Way to demonstrate/present the "How"	

Group 4

Standard: Use precise language and domain-specific vocabulary to inform about or explain the topic.

What	How
Describe the three branches of government	Interview or role play
Content Objective:	**Language Objective:**
Way to demonstrate/present the "How"	

Group 5

Standard: Determine the central ideas or conclusions of a text; summarize complex concepts, processes, or information presented in a text by paraphrasing them in simpler but still accurate terms.

What	How
Explain the water cycle	Musical: song or chant
Content Objective:	**Language Objective:**
Way to demonstrate/present the "How"	

Group 6

Standard: Acquire and use accurately grade-appropriate general academic and domain-specific words and phrases, including those that signal contrast, addition, and other logical relationships (for example, however, although, nevertheless, similarly, moreover, in addition).

What	How
Key vocabulary in math, English, or science	TPR (Total Physical Response) — Using gestures and words
Content Objective:	**Language Objective:**
Way to demonstrate/present the "How"	

Let's Get Planning: Practice & Application

Record your ideas for incorporating the features of Practice & Application into your lesson plan.

What hands-on materials and/or manipulatives will you provide for students to practice using new content knowledge?

_____

_____

_____

_____

_____

What activities will you provide for students to apply content and language knowledge in the classroom?

_____

_____

_____

_____

_____

What activities will you include that integrate all language skills (i.e., reading, writing, listening, and speaking)?

_____

_____

_____

_____

_____

Practice & Application: Wrap-Up

Why is it important for practice and application to be tied directly to a lesson's objectives?

_____

_____

_____

_____

_____

_____

_____

Find a partner wearing the same color shoes as you and share.

LESSON DELIVERY
(*MCC4*, Chapter 8)

Wright Family Story

Each time the word <u>Wright</u> or <u>right</u> is read, pass the object to the <u>right</u>. Each time the word <u>left</u> is read, pass the object to the <u>left</u>.

Mrs. <u>Wright</u> eyed her grocery list carefully. "There won't be anything <u>left</u> of our budget after shopping" she said. Mr. <u>Wright</u> looked up from his paper and said: "That's all <u>right</u> my dear, if there isn't anything <u>left</u>, I'll be happy if the <u>Wright</u> family makes it through the month."

As Mr. <u>Wright</u> turned back to his paper he said, "Have you the <u>right</u> gift for Sue <u>Wright's</u> birthday? She's been pretty lonely since her daughter <u>left</u> home <u>right</u> after she married. Uncle Tom <u>left</u> her a lot of money, but she does not enjoy life <u>right</u>."

Son, Ed <u>Wright</u>, was studying in the corner of the <u>left</u> side of the fireplace. "I wish Sue <u>Wright</u> would ask me the <u>right</u> way to spend the money."

Mary <u>Wright</u> said, "she would not have much <u>left</u> if she did. Your weekly allowance is gone before you get it <u>right</u> in your hands."

"And I suppose you have all yours <u>left</u> Miss Mary," said Ed <u>Wright</u>.

"I don't have it all <u>left</u> but I have enough <u>left</u> to buy toys I like," Mary <u>Wright</u> said.

Just then the doorbell rang. Mary <u>Wright</u> ran to answer the door, and the postman <u>left</u> a special delivery letter for the <u>Wright</u> family. She took it to Father <u>Wright</u> and he opened it. Inside was a letter and four new ten dollar bills. Mr. <u>Wright</u> shouted, "It's from Aunt <u>Wright</u> saying she has <u>left</u> town and decided to go <u>right</u> to her daughter's house."

"Say, she's all <u>right</u>" shouted Eddie <u>Wright</u>. "Bless her heart," said Mother <u>Wright</u>.

"How wonderful of her," said Mary <u>Wright</u>.

"It makes each of us <u>right</u> happy to think she wrote us before she <u>left</u>," declared Father <u>Wright</u>. "At least it's all <u>right</u> with the <u>Wright</u> family."

Wright Family Exercise

What was the passage about?

_____

_____

_____

_____

_____

How did you feel as the passage was read?

_____

_____

_____

_____

_____

What could the reader have done differently to help you comprehend the content of the passage?

_____

_____

_____

_____

_____

Let's Reflect on Lesson Objectives

1. Why is it necessary to share the objectives with students at the beginning of a lesson?

2. Why is it a good idea to review the objectives at the end of each lesson?

3. What are some factors that contribute to high levels of student engagement?

4. How do objectives affect the pacing of a lesson?

Lesson Delivery Features

23. **Content objectives** clearly supported by lesson delivery

24. **Language objectives** clearly supported by lesson delivery

25. **Students engaged** approximately 90% to 100% of the period

26. **Pacing** of the lesson appropriate to students' ability levels

(MCC4, pp. 193–197)

How do you keep students engaged?

What are some methods you use in your classroom to promote student engagement?

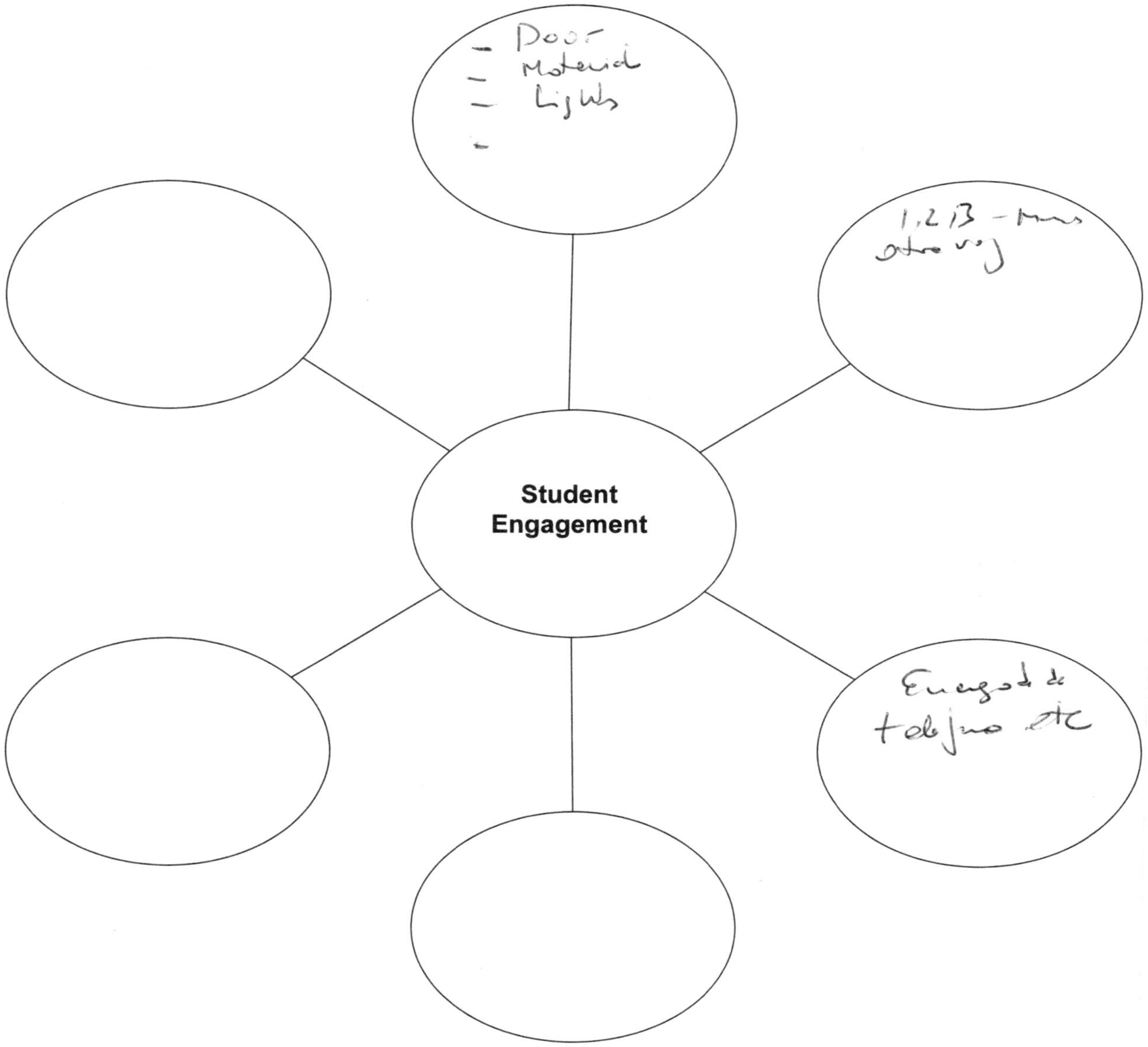

Factors Contributing to High Levels of Student Engagement

- Well-planned lessons

- Clear explanation of academic tasks or instruction

- Appropriate amount of time spent on an academic task

- Strong classroom management skills

- Opportunities for students to apply learning in a meaningful way

- Active student involvement

- Lesson design meets the language and learning needs of students

The Sheltered Instruction Observation Protocol (SIOP®)

From *MCC4*, pp. 288–293

Observer(s): _____   Teacher: _____

Date: _____   School: _____

Grade: _____   Class/Topic: _____

ESL Level: _____   Lesson: Multi-day   Single-day   (*circle one*)

Total Points Possible: 120 (Subtract 4 points for each NA given: _____)

Total Points Earned: _____   Percentage Score: _____

Directions: Circle the number that best reflects what you observe in a sheltered lesson. You may give a score from 0–4 (or NA on selected items). Cite under "Comments" specific examples of the behaviors observed.

Lesson Preparation

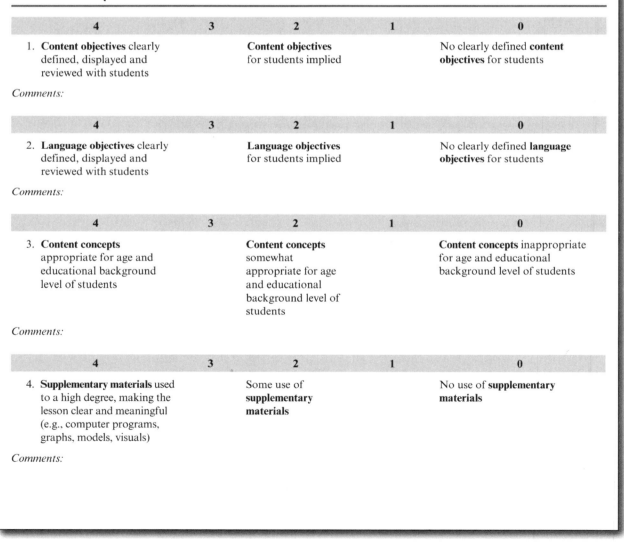

4	3	2	1	0
1. **Content objectives** clearly defined, displayed and reviewed with students		**Content objectives** for students implied		No clearly defined **content objectives** for students

Comments:

4	3	2	1	0
2. **Language objectives** clearly defined, displayed and reviewed with students		**Language objectives** for students implied		No clearly defined **language objectives** for students

Comments:

4	3	2	1	0
3. **Content concepts** appropriate for age and educational background level of students		**Content concepts** somewhat appropriate for age and educational background level of students		**Content concepts** inappropriate for age and educational background level of students

Comments:

4	3	2	1	0
4. **Supplementary materials** used to a high degree, making the lesson clear and meaningful (e.g., computer programs, graphs, models, visuals)		Some use of **supplementary materials**		No use of **supplementary materials**

Comments:

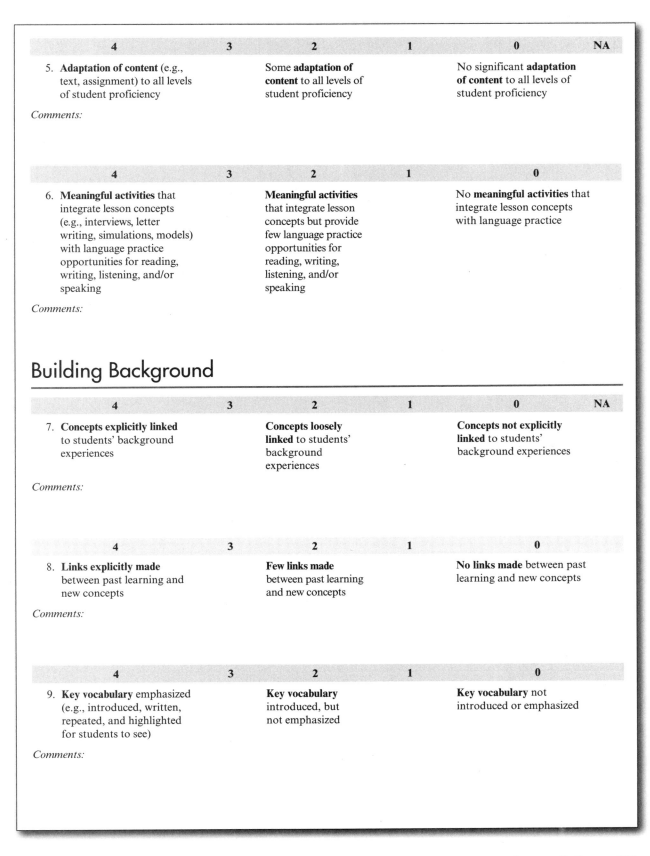

4	3	2	1	0	NA

5. **Adaptation of content** (e.g., text, assignment) to all levels of student proficiency

Some **adaptation of content** to all levels of student proficiency

No significant **adaptation of content** to all levels of student proficiency

Comments:

4	3	2	1	0

6. **Meaningful activities** that integrate lesson concepts (e.g., interviews, letter writing, simulations, models) with language practice opportunities for reading, writing, listening, and/or speaking

Meaningful activities that integrate lesson concepts but provide few language practice opportunities for reading, writing, listening, and/or speaking

No **meaningful activities** that integrate lesson concepts with language practice

Comments:

Building Background

4	3	2	1	0	NA

7. **Concepts explicitly linked** to students' background experiences

Concepts loosely linked to students' background experiences

Concepts not explicitly linked to students' background experiences

Comments:

4	3	2	1	0

8. **Links explicitly made** between past learning and new concepts

Few links made between past learning and new concepts

No links made between past learning and new concepts

Comments:

4	3	2	1	0

9. **Key vocabulary** emphasized (e.g., introduced, written, repeated, and highlighted for students to see)

Key vocabulary introduced, but not emphasized

Key vocabulary not introduced or emphasized

Comments:

Comprehensible Input

4	3	2	1	0
10. **Speech** appropriate for students' proficiency levels (e.g., slower rate, enunciation, and simple sentence structure for beginners)		**Speech** sometimes inappropriate for students' proficiency levels		**Speech** inappropriate for students' proficiency levels

Comments:

4	3	2	1	0
11. **Clear explanation** of academic tasks		**Unclear** explanation of academic tasks		**No** explanation of academic tasks

Comments:

4	3	2	1	0
12. **A variety of techniques** used to make content concepts clear (e.g., modeling, visuals, hands-on activities, demonstrations, gestures, body language)		Some techniques used to make content concepts clear		No **techniques** used to make concepts clear

Comments:

Strategies

4	3	2	1	0
13. Ample opportunities provided for students to use **learning strategies**		Inadequate opportunities provided for students to use **learning strategies**		No opportunity provided for students to use **learning strategies**

Comments:

4	3	2	1	0
14. **Scaffolding techniques** consistently used, assisting and supporting student understanding (e.g., think-alouds)		**Scaffolding techniques** occasionally used		**Scaffolding techniques** not used

Comments:

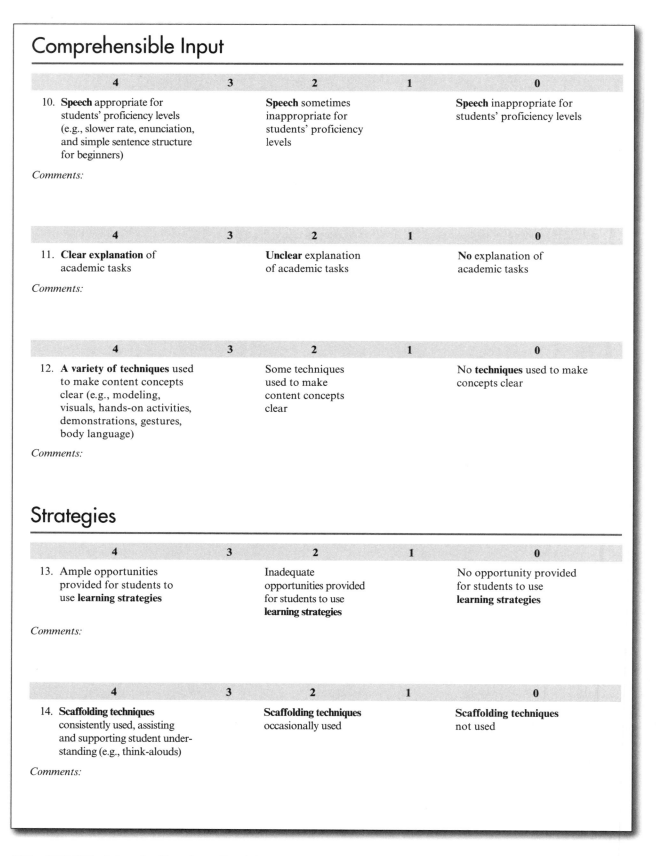

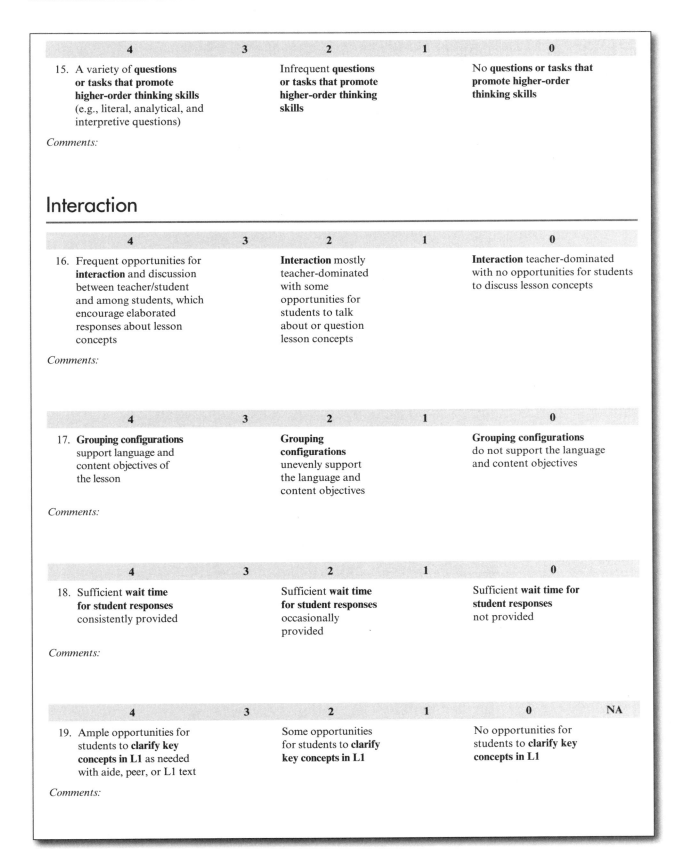

4	3	2	1	0
15. A variety of **questions or tasks that promote higher-order thinking skills** (e.g., literal, analytical, and interpretive questions)		Infrequent **questions or tasks that promote higher-order thinking skills**		No **questions or tasks that promote higher-order thinking skills**

Comments:

Interaction

4	3	2	1	0
16. Frequent opportunities for **interaction** and discussion between teacher/student and among students, which encourage elaborated responses about lesson concepts		**Interaction** mostly teacher-dominated with some opportunities for students to talk about or question lesson concepts		**Interaction** teacher-dominated with no opportunities for students to discuss lesson concepts

Comments:

4	3	2	1	0
17. **Grouping configurations** support language and content objectives of the lesson		**Grouping configurations** unevenly support the language and content objectives		**Grouping configurations** do not support the language and content objectives

Comments:

4	3	2	1	0
18. Sufficient **wait time for student responses** consistently provided		Sufficient **wait time for student responses** occasionally provided		Sufficient **wait time for student responses** not provided

Comments:

4	3	2	1	0	NA
19. Ample opportunities for students to **clarify key concepts in L1** as needed with aide, peer, or L1 text		Some opportunities for students to **clarify key concepts in L1**		No opportunities for students to **clarify key concepts in L1**	

Comments:

Practice & Application

4	3	2	1	0	NA
20. **Hands-on materials and/or manipulatives** provided for students to practice using new content knowledge		Few **hands-on materials and/or manipulatives** provided for students to practice using new content knowledge		No **hands-on materials and/or manipulatives** provided for students to practice using new content knowledge	

Comments:

4	3	2	1	0	NA
21. Activities provided for students to **apply content and language knowledge** in the classroom		Activities provided for students to **apply** either **content or language knowledge** in the classroom		No activities provided for students to **apply content and language knowledge** in the classroom	

Comments:

4	3	2	1	0
22. Activities integrate all **language skills** (i.e., reading, writing, listening, and speaking)		Activities integrate some **language skills**		Activities do not integrate **language skills**

Comments:

Lesson Delivery

4	3	2	1	0
23. **Content objectives** clearly supported by lesson delivery		**Content objectives** somewhat supported by lesson delivery		**Content objectives** not supported by lesson delivery

Comments:

4	3	2	1	0
24. **Language objectives** clearly supported by lesson delivery		**Language objectives** somewhat supported by lesson delivery		**Language objectives** not supported by lesson delivery

Comments:

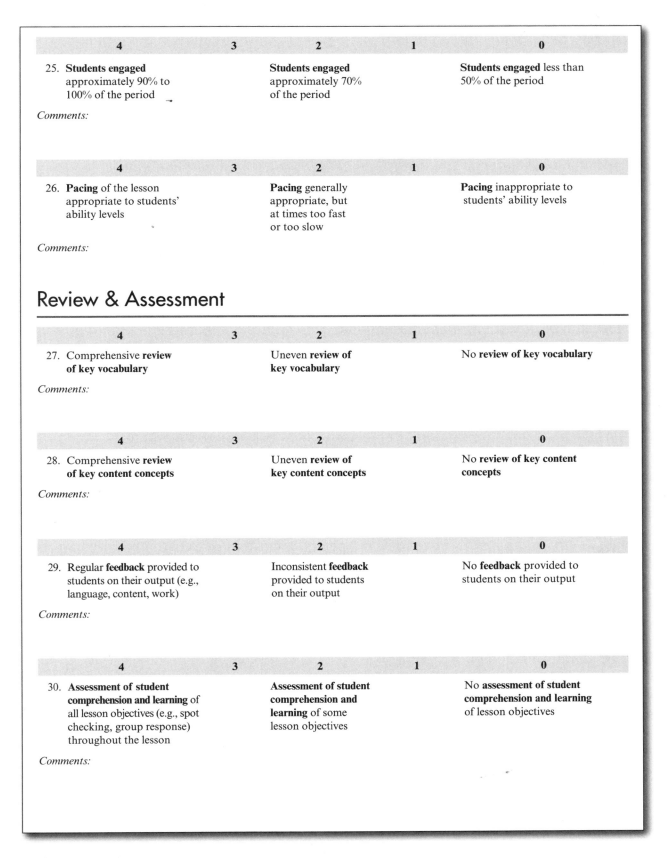

4	3	2	1	0
25. **Students engaged** approximately 90% to 100% of the period		**Students engaged** approximately 70% of the period		**Students engaged** less than 50% of the period

Comments:

4	3	2	1	0
26. **Pacing** of the lesson appropriate to students' ability levels		**Pacing** generally appropriate, but at times too fast or too slow		**Pacing** inappropriate to students' ability levels

Comments:

Review & Assessment

4	3	2	1	0
27. Comprehensive **review of key vocabulary**		Uneven **review of key vocabulary**		No **review of key vocabulary**

Comments:

4	3	2	1	0
28. Comprehensive **review of key content concepts**		Uneven **review of key content concepts**		No **review of key content concepts**

Comments:

4	3	2	1	0
29. Regular **feedback** provided to students on their output (e.g., language, content, work)		Inconsistent **feedback** provided to students on their output		No **feedback** provided to students on their output

Comments:

4	3	2	1	0
30. **Assessment of student comprehension and learning** of all lesson objectives (e.g., spot checking, group response) throughout the lesson		**Assessment of student comprehension and learning** of some lesson objectives		No **assessment of student comprehension and learning** of lesson objectives

Comments:

Video: What does Lesson Delivery look like?

As you observe the classroom video, note evidence of any of the Lesson Delivery features that are incorporated in this part of the lesson.

_____

_____

_____

_____

_____

_____

_____

_____

_____

_____

_____

_____

_____

_____

_____

_____

_____

Lesson Delivery: What did you observe?

In your groups, discuss . . .	On your own, reflect on . . .
How were the content and language objectives clearly supported by the delivery of the lesson?	What will be challenging for you in supporting your content and language objectives?
How did the lesson promote a high level of student engagement?	What will be challenging for you in promoting student engagement?
How was the pacing of the lesson appropriate to the students' ability levels?	What will be challenging for you in determining the pacing of your lessons?

SIOP Lesson—Lesson Delivery

Grade/Class/Subject:
Teacher: Kendra Moreno
Unit/Theme: Chibi: A True Story fromJapan (Day One)
Content Objective(s): SWBAT(Students will be able to) distinguish fact fromopinion (within a reading selection).
Language Objective(s): SWBATorally defend their position on whether a statement is fact or opinion.

Standards:
Strand 3: Comprehending Informational Text; Concept 3 Persuasive Text; PO1 Distinguish fact fromopinion

---

Key Vocabulary

➤ Fact
➤ Opinion

Supplementary Materials

➤ Fact/opinion poster fromDanger: Icebergs
➤ Inside/outside circle cards and overhead
➤ Tickets out

SIOP Features

Preparation

_X_	Adaptation of Content
_X_	Links to Background
_X_	Links to Past Learning
_X_	Strategies incorporated

Scaffolding

___	Modeling
___	Guided practice
___	Independent practice
___	Comprehensible input

Grouping Options

_X_	Whole class
_X_	Small groups
_X_	Partners
_X_	Independent

Integration of Processes

_X_	Reading
_X_	Writing
_X_	Speaking
_X_	Listening

Application

_X_	Hands-on
_X_	Meaningful
_X_	Linked to objectives
_X_	Promotes engagement

Assessment

_X_	Individual
_X_	Group
_X_	Written
_X_	Oral

Lesson Sequence

Building Background

➤ So how's the weather today? (Call on several students and list their responses on the board). TW (teacher will) contribute, "I think it's gloomy." Next, the TWwrite, "It's 64 degrees outside" on the board.
➤ Help the students recall that we talked extensively about fact and opinion when we read the selection Danger: Icebergs last quarter. Who recalls that story? Hang the poster that was generated for that selection and reviewthe definition of fact and opinion and the example about the Titanic.("The Titanic was the largest (fact) and most beautiful (opinion) ship ever built.")
➤ "Looking back on our statements about the weather, which are facts and which are opinions?"
➤ Introduce today's objectives.
➤ Students will turn to the story in their book that we are reading during our Guided Reading block. As a class, chorally read the first paragraph on page 168. TWwrite, "The duck is ___." on the board. Beneath, write yellow, swimming, scraggly, and cute. TW lead a discussion about scraggly.
➤ Ask students: "Which words could we put in the blank to make the statement a fact? Why? Which words would make the statement an opinion? Why?"
➤ "Let's read another passage fromthe story." Turn to page 174. The TWread through page 175. "What opinion do the people have when they see Oka-san marching her ducklings back and forth?" (Seek and Find question) We can infer that the people think that she is crazy. Ask students why that is an opinion.

➤ There is another opinion in this paragraph. TW point out to the students that the word "ideal" is another way of saying perfect. When the author says, "The moat is an ideal place for growing ducklings" I know that this is something that cannot be proved. It's what someone thinks or feels. What is ideal for one person may not be ideal for another.

Practice & Application

Guided
➤ To practice the concept of fact and opinion, SW (students will) participate in an inside/outside circle. Each student will be given a statement. They will read it to their partner and ask, "Is this a fact or an opinion?" The student must give their response and then orally defend their position. Rotate a total of 8 times. TW monitor the activity closely and provide feedback on student output.
➤ Students return to their seats. Review and discuss the 8 statements on the overhead.

Independent
➤ Working with a partner, students will read an informational article about ducks' feet and food. They will complete a chart distinguishing fact and opinion. They are to discuss with one another how they determined which statements were facts and which were opinions.

Review & Assessment
➤ Orally review content and language objectives with students.
➤ Tickets Out (see below).

Fact and Opinion Statements for Inside/Outside Circle
1. The United States is the greatest country in the world.
2. There are 50 states in the United States.
3. Computers are the greatest modern invention.
4. Sound travels through sound waves.
5. It is more important to have good vision than it is to have good hearing.
6. Students who do not finish their homework are lazy.
7. I think that Ms. Moreno is too strict.
8. A vibration is when something moves back and forth very rapidly.

Tickets Out
Label each statement fact or opinion. Tell how you know.
1. The mother duck had ten ducklings.
2. The ducklings were beautiful.
3. The ducklings were light yellow.
4. Ducks are the best pets.

Lesson Delivery Ratings

....

Lesson Delivery

4	3	2	1	0
23. **Content objectives** clearly supported by lesson delivery		**Content objectives** somewhat supported by lesson delivery		**Content objectives** not supported by lesson delivery

Comments:

4	3	2	1	0
24. **Language objectives** clearly supported by lesson delivery		**Language objectives** somewhat supported by lesson delivery		**Language objectives** not supported by lesson delivery

Comments:

4	3	2	1	0
25. **Students engaged** approximately 90% to 100% of the period		**Students engaged** approximately 70% of the period		**Students engaged** less than 50% of the period

Comments:

4	3	2	1	0
26. **Pacing** of the lesson appropriate to students' ability levels		**Pacing** generally appropriate, but at times too fast or too slow		**Pacing** inappropriate to students' ability levels

Comments:

(*MCC4*, pp. 292–293)

Let's Get Planning: Lesson Delivery

Record your ideas for incorporating the features of Lesson Delivery into your lesson plan.

How will you clearly support the content and language objectives throughout the delivery of the lesson?

_____

_____

_____

_____

_____

_____

How will you ensure that the lesson promotes a high level of student engagement (90%–100%)?

_____

_____

_____

_____

_____

_____

How will you ensure that the pacing of the lesson is appropriate to the students' ability levels?

_____

_____

_____

_____

_____

_____

REVIEW & ASSESSMENT
(*MCC4*, Chapter 9)

Review & Assessment Features

27. Comprehensive **review of key vocabulary**

28. Comprehensive **review of key content concepts**

29. Regular **feedback** provided to students on their output

30. **Assessment of student comprehension and learning** of all lesson objectives throughout the lesson

(MCC4, pp. 214–220)

Review & Assessment Activity Ideas

1. Review Vocabulary

   _____

   _____

   _____

2. Review Content Concepts

   _____

   _____

   _____

3. Favorite 5-Minute Wrap-Ups

   _____

   _____

   _____

4. Provide Informal Feedback to Students

   _____

   _____

   _____

5. Test-Taking Strategies for Students

   _____

   _____

   _____

6. Quick Assessment of Student Learning

   _____

   _____

   _____

Classroom Connections: Simultaneous Roundtable

Activity Directions:

1. Write each topic on a separate piece of paper and distribute.

2. Students record what they know about their given topic.

3. When time is called (every 4 minutes), students pass their paper to the person on their right, read what has been written, and add to it.

4. Repeat the process until students receive their original paper back.

5. Students choose two items from their paper to share with the whole group.

Could you use Simultaneous Roundtable in your classroom? If so, how?

_____

_____

_____

_____

_____

_____

_____

How does Simultaneous Roundtable allow the teacher to review and assess student learning?

_____

_____

_____

_____

_____

_____

_____

_____

© 2012 Pearson, Inc.

Review & Assessment: Analyzing a Lesson Vignette

- In what way was the key vocabulary reviewed in the lesson?

  _____

  _____

  _____

  _____

- In what ways were the key content concepts reviewed in the lesson?

  _____

  _____

  _____

  _____

- How was regular feedback provided to students on their output throughout the lesson?

  _____

  _____

  _____

  _____

- How was student comprehension and student learning of all lesson objectives assessed?

  _____

  _____

  _____

  _____

Review & Assessment Ratings

....

Review & Assessment

4	3	2	1	0
27. Comprehensive **review of key vocabulary**		Uneven **review of key vocabulary**		No **review of key vocabulary**

Comments:

4	3	2	1	0
28. Comprehensive **review of key content concepts**		Uneven **review of key content concepts**		No **review of key content concepts**

Comments:

4	3	2	1	0
29. Regular **feedback** provided to students on their output (e.g., language, content, work)		Inconsistent **feedback** provided to students on their output		No **feedback** provided to students on their output

Comments:

4	3	2	1	0
30. **Assessment of student comprehension and learning** of all lesson objectives (e.g., spot checking, group response) throughout the lesson		**Assessment of student comprehension and learning** of some lesson objectives		No **assessment of student comprehension and learning** of lesson objectives

Comments:

(*MCC4*, p. 293)

Let's Get Planning: Review & Assessment

Record your ideas for incorporating the features of Review & Assessment into your lesson plan.

How will you review the key vocabulary in your lesson?

_____

_____

_____

_____

_____

How will you review the key content concepts in your lesson?

_____

_____

_____

_____

_____

How will you provide regular feedback to students on their output?

_____

_____

_____

_____

_____

How will you assess student comprehension and student learning of all lesson objectives throughout the lesson?

_____

_____

_____

_____

_____

LESSON PLANNING

SIOP Lesson Plan Template 1

SIOP Lesson Title: **Grade:**

Content Standard(s):

Key Vocabulary:
Content: Subject Specific and Technical Terms:

General Academic: Cross-Curricular Terms/Process & Function:

Word Parts: Roots and Affixes:

HOTS:

Supplementary Materials:

Explicit Connections to Prior Knowledge and Experiences/Building Background:

Explicit Connections to Past Learning:

Content Objective(s): SWBAT: SF (if needed): Language Objective(s): SWBAT: SF (if needed):	Meaningful Activities: Sequence	Review/Assessment:

Wrap-Up: This must include the review of the content and language objectives, followed by teacher choice of final wrap-up to the lesson.

(Developed by Melissa Castillo & Nicole Teyechea, as cited in *Making Content Comprehensible for English Learners: The SIOP® Model,* 4th ed., pp. 301–302.)

SIOP Features Checklist

Directions:

1. Find a partner.
2. Partner 1: Share your lesson plan.
3. Partner 2: Using the SIOP Features Checklist, identify the SIOP features included in your partner's plan.
4. Switch roles and repeat so that you both share.

Lesson Preparation

- ❑ **Content objectives** clearly defined, displayed, and reviewed with students
- ❑ **Language objectives** clearly defined, displayed, and reviewed with students
- ❑ **Content concepts** appropriate for age and educational background level of students
- ❑ **Supplementary materials** used to a high degree, making the lesson clear and meaningful
- ❑ **Adaptation of content** to all levels of student proficiency
- ❑ **Meaningful activities** that integrate lesson concepts with language practice opportunities for reading, writing, listening, and/or speaking

Building Background

- ❑ **Concepts explicitly linked** to students' background experiences
- ❑ **Links explicitly made** between past learning and new concepts
- ❑ **Key vocabulary** emphasized

Comprehensible Input

- ❑ **Speech** appropriate for students' proficiency levels
- ❑ **Clear explanation** of academic tasks
- ❑ **A variety of techniques** used to make content concepts clear

Strategies

- ❑ Ample opportunities provided for students to use **learning strategies**
- ❑ **Scaffolding techniques** consistently used, assisting and supporting student understanding
- ❑ A variety of **questions or tasks that promote higher-order thinking skills**

Interaction

- ❑ Frequent opportunities for **interaction** and discussion between teacher/student and among students, which encourage elaborated responses about lesson concepts
- ❑ **Grouping configurations** support language and content objectives of the lesson
- ❑ Sufficient **wait time for student responses** consistently provided
- ❑ Ample opportunities for students to **clarify key concepts in L1** as needed with aide, peer, or L1 text

Practice & Application

- ❑ **Hands-on materials and/or manipulatives** provided for students to practice using new content knowledge
- ❑ Activities provided for students to **apply content and language knowledge** in the classroom
- ❑ Activities integrate all **language skills** (i.e., reading, writing, listening, and speaking)

Lesson Delivery

- ❑ **Content objectives** clearly supported by lesson delivery
- ❑ **Language objectives** clearly supported by lesson delivery
- ❑ **Students engaged** approximately 90% to 100% of the period
- ❑ **Pacing** of the lesson appropriate to students' ability levels

Review & Assessment

- ❑ Comprehensive **review of key vocabulary**
- ❑ Comprehensive **review of key content concepts**
- ❑ Regular **feedback** provided to students on their output
- ❑ **Assessment of student comprehension and learning** of all lesson objectives throughout the lesson

Lesson Implementation Reflection

After you've taught the lesson you planned with your colleagues, use this page to note your reflections as part of the "plan-teach-analyze-revise" teaching cycle.

Lesson Title: _____   Date: _____

List the key modifications that you planned and implemented in your lesson to address each feature. Note the effect of the modifications that you implemented on your English learners' content comprehension.

What did you try?	What happened?

Based on your reflection, what are some changes you would make in the lesson to help English learners meet the lesson objectives?

_____

_____

_____

_____

_____

IMPLEMENTING THE SIOP MODEL

SIOP Model Implementation Action Plan

1. Highlight/underline the component you/your school district will address first as you work toward fully implementing the SIOP Model in your classroom:

Lesson Preparation	Building Background	Comprehensible Input
Strategies	Interaction	Practice & Application
Lesson Delivery	Review & Assessment	

2. Identify the action steps you will take to implement your chosen component.

    _____

    _____

    _____

    _____

    _____

    _____

    _____

    _____

    _____

    _____

3. List anticipated needs/resources.

    _____

    _____

    _____

    _____

    _____

    _____

    _____

    _____

    _____

    _____

4. Develop a simple timeline for your action steps over the next two months.

_____

_____

_____

_____

_____

_____

_____

_____

_____

5. Identify at least one implementation question or challenge you have.

_____

_____

_____

_____

_____

_____

_____

_____

_____

6. Brainstorm possible solutions.

_____

_____

_____

_____

_____

_____

_____

_____

SIOP Model Implementation Action Plan Support

Describe one or two things your group will do to support each other in implementing the SIOP components in your classrooms. Identify who will do what, and when.

What? (Actions)	Who Is Responsible?	When?

1. Think about what resources and support you will need from your administrator and list them here.

   _____

   _____

2. What is at least one step you can take to get these resources and support from your administrator?

   _____

   _____

APPENDIX

SIOP Lesson Plan Template 1

SIOP Lesson Title:	**Grade:**

Content Standard(s):

Key Vocabulary:	**Supplementary Materials:**
Content: Subject Specific and Technical Terms:	
General Academic: Cross-Curricular Terms/Process & Function:	
Word Parts: Roots and Affixes:	
HOTS:	

Explicit Connections to Prior Knowledge and Experiences/Building Background:

Explicit Connections to Past Learning:

Content Objective(s): SWBAT:	Meaningful Activities: Sequence	Review/Assessment:
SF (if needed): **Language Objective(s):** SWBAT: SF (if needed):		

Wrap-Up: This must include the review of the content and language objectives, followed by teacher choice of final wrap-up to the lesson.

(Developed by Melissa Castillo & Nicole Teyechea, as cited in *Making Content Comprehensible for English Learners: The SIOP® Model,* 4th ed., pp. 301–302.)

References

Common Core State Standards. (2012.) About the standards. Retrieved from http://www.corestandards.org/about-the-standards

Echevarría, J., & Graves, A. (2011). *Sheltered content instruction: Teaching English learners with diverse abilities.* (4th ed.). Boston, MA: Pearson Allyn and Bacon.

Echevarría, J., Richards, C., Canges, R., & Francis, D. (2011). Using the SIOP® Model to promote the acquisition of language and science concepts with English learners. *Bilingual Research Journal 34*(3), 334–351.

Echevarría, J., Richards-Tutor, C., Chinn, V., & Ratleff, P. (2011). Did they get it? The role of fidelity in improving teaching for English learners. *Journal of Adolescent and Adult Literacy 54*(6), 425–434.

Echevarría, J., Vogt, M.E., & Short, D. (2013). *Making content comprehensible for English learners: The SIOP® Model.* (4th ed.). Boston, MA: Pearson Allyn and Bacon.

Steinberg, A., & Almeida, C. (2004). *The dropout crisis: Promising approaches in prevention and recovery.* Boston: Jobs for the Future.

Vogt, M.E., & Echevarría, J. (2008). *99 ideas and activities for teaching English learners with the SIOP® Model.* Boston, MA: Pearson Allyn and Bacon.

Xiao-yan. (2006). *Teacher talk and EFL in university classrooms.* MA Dissertation, retrieved from www.asian-efl-journal.com/thesis_Ma_Xiaou.pdf.

Notes

Certificate of Completion

Awarded to

_____

for the completion of

SIOP® TRAINING FOR TEACHERS

School: _____

District: _____

Date: _____

Deborah A. Estrada
_____
Deborah A. Estrada
Director of Services

SHELTERED INSTRUCTION
SIOP®
OBSERVATION PROTOCOL

PEARSON

ALWAYS LEARNING